THEODORE
ROOSEVELT

People You Should Know

THEODORE ROOSEVELT

Naturalist / Statesman

by JOYCE BLACKBURN

Illustrated by David Cunningham

ZONDERVAN PUBLISHING HOUSE
GRAND RAPIDS, MICHIGAN

For
Earl M. Anderson
with gratitude

PART ONE
1858 - 1886

1

It was not the first parade the boy had watched from his grandfather's big house. It *was* the parade he would always remember best. On this afternoon of April 25, 1865, Theodore Roosevelt was only seven years old. But he knew why this parade was unlike the others.

Since Grandfather Roosevelt's house stood at the corner of Broadway and 14th Street, Theodore could see in all directions. And wherever he looked there were people. They jammed the sidewalks and curbs, doorways and windows, balconies and roofs. Everyone in New York City was waiting. There were no cheers nor songs. These people stood silent. Tears wet their faces. Even the measured tread of the soldiers marching by seemed hushed. Many of the soldiers were crying too.

Bells tolled slowly. Cannons boomed somberly. The drums kept time. Drums muffled in black. It would take two hours for the 20,000 troops of the Union Army to pass; cavalry, artillery and the infantry with guns reversed, the regimental bands playing a march for the dead.

Theodore watched and felt sorry for the people. This was the funeral procession for the 17th President of the United States.

"Why are they turning, Grandfather?" Theodore whispered.

"Because from here they go to 5th Avenue, then to 34th Street, to 9th Avenue, to the Hudson River Railroad depot."

Theodore knew the procession had come from City

Hall. Now the marchers turned off Broadway onto 14th Street. Across the street was Union Square. A memorial ceremony was to be held there later.

"I see more horses coming." Theodore leaned out the window. "There are sixteen. I can count them."

All of the Roosevelts in the big house that day watched with the boy as the horses came nearer, each led by a groom dressed in black. No one spoke as they passed pulling the high domed glass hearse with its plumes of black, its draped American flag, its long narrow coffin. It had been ten days since a mad man shot Abraham Lincoln.

"Abraham Lincoln Our Emancipator" — that's what Theodore read on a wide banner. A banner carried by the Negroes at the end of the procession. There were 2,000 of them.

"They have lost their champion," Grandfather said.

"And my hero is gone," said the boy.

2

That night, alone in his own room, Theodore could not go to sleep. Watching the long procession from the window had been a risk. Excitement was always bad for his asthma. As often happened, he must sit up in bed in order to get his breath, and the coughing made him tired. His mind was wide awake, though, his thoughts a jumble of bewildering questions. The funeral parade and the sudden loss of the President bewildered him, coming so soon after the celebrations of recent days.

Theodore counted back to April 14, Good Friday. That was when the President had been shot. Only the day before, red, white and blue bunting had hung from every place of business, every lamp post. Bands marched up and down Broadway playing "Rally 'Round the Flag, Boys," and flags appeared by the thousands. The crowds laughed and sang. It had been that way since the morning of April 10th. The war was over — The Civil War. The War Between The States — it had ended. Fireworks crackled. The tugs on the river blew their whistles. Every bell in New York City rang. Dignified officials joined the noise-making with tin horns and cowbells. On the floor of the Stock Exchange business men broke into singing, "Praise God From Whom All Blessings Flow..."

No one was more jubilant than the boy, Theodore Roosevelt. He may have understood more about the War than most boys his age, because it was discussed often by his parents and relatives. His mother was from an old Southern family, the Bullochs of Georgia. Her two brothers had fought in the Confederate navy. Admiral

11

James Dunwoodie Bulloch had arranged for the building of the famous warship *Alabama*. Midshipman Irvine Bulloch, fired the last gun before the *Alabama* was sunk in its battle with the *Kearsarge*. Naturally, Mrs. Roosevelt had sympathized with the South. But Theodore's father was a strong Lincoln Republican. He had carried out missions for the government many times, missions that took him to the Union troops in the front lines.

Both sides of the slavery issue were talked about by the Roosevelts, and yet nothing changed the atmosphere of love and fun and gentleness that had surrounded Theodore from the moment his life began, October 27, 1858. The Civil War did not change that. Theodore, his brother, Elliott, his sisters, Anna and Corrine, listened to their parents and the visitors who came to their home at 28 East 20th Street, but they were never exposed to bitter disagreements. Even the long arguments about slavery did not end in anger.

Since Theodore was ill much of the time, unable to play as actively as the other children, he listened more to the grownup talk. Listened and decided he was on his father's side. Father disapproves of cruelty, Theodore thought, whether it's toward children or animals or Negroes. He thinks President Lincoln is right. America is for all the people. I agree. Father and I are Lincoln men.

Theodore sat up in the dark of that sad night, thinking about his hero who was gone, and he was filled with wonder at all that had happened in just fifteen days.

3

Some nights the boy could think of nothing except the next breath. It was as though he were being attacked by a monstrous shadow that towered like a wave above him. Instead of crashing down from the ceiling, it ballooned around him, suffocating, smothering, wrapping its darkness around his throat, his chest, his ribs. He would claw and wrestle and pull until a little gasp of air expanded his lungs, then the pain again, the choking, strangling, squeezing attack. No one could stop it. No one could help him. He was in this battle alone, and sometimes he was sure it would end forever if he didn't get that next breath.

While the boy was very young, Theodore's father would hold his son in his powerful arms and pace the floor until the attack subsided. Now that Theodore was older they had a kind of game. When the coughing was especially bad, his father would bring warm afghans and carriage robes, wrap the boy in them, not tightly, loosely, then carry him down to the street where a groom waited with the high phaeton and two teams of long-tailed horses.

"I want to take Master Theodore for a turn through the park, Waters," Mr. Roosevelt said to the groom. After settling the boy on the seat, he would flick the horses ever so lightly with the whip and off they would clatter.

"Father, when may I drive four-in-hand?" Theodore asked.

"As soon as you are strong enough," Mr. Roosevelt

said gently. "Right now try to get some of this cool fresh air. Breathe deeply."

Faster and faster the tandem teams sped; faster and faster the street lamps danced past until in Theodore's imagination the horses had wings, the phaeton no longer touched the ground; Theodore was a god in space — free of the shadow, the smothering tightness.

He gulped the clean air, coughed, drank in the night, laughed. He was winning, winning, winning...

4

One morning after Mr. Roosevelt had conducted family prayers, he said, "I have something to show you, Theodore." The boy, small for his age, looked unbelievably frail as he followed his tall and handsome father through the house to an outside porch.

"In order to exercise properly, you need a gymnasium," Mr. Roosevelt said, leading Theodore onto the porch which had been remodeled and equipped according to his father's instructions. "Well, what do you think of it?"

"I think it's the keenest gymnasium in the whole world, Father!" Theodore grasped the parallel bars and turned a somersault. But he looked at the punching-bag uncertainly.

"With a lot of work and discipline, I know you can build your body into a healthy partner for your mind, Theodore. Even though you haven't been well enough to go to school, you've studied and read more than some of the children who do go. We're going to find out if your body can catch up with your good brain. You can do exercise just the same as you do your lessons, and you'll enjoy it more if you'll do it wholeheartedly."

Theodore knew that was the way his father performed every duty, and more than anything, he wanted to be like him. Looking Mr. Roosevelt straight in the eyes, the boy said, "I'll do it!"

A determined struggle began. Every day Theodore was not kept in bed by illness he worked out in the gymnasium. At first he could exercise for only a few minutes. The muscles in his arms and legs trembled with weakness; tumbling or lifting dumbbells started the coughing again; unable to overpower the punching-bag, he would forget to duck away from it, and it kept knocking him off his feet. Some of those sessions were utterly disheartening. But Theodore went back to the gymnasium and tried again and again, until finally he was strong enough to work out regularly and for as long as he liked.

Besides exercising, he studied his lessons with a tutor and found time for favorite enthusiasms, such as reading. He read every adventure book he could lay his hands on. Years afterward, he remembered them so vividly he could tell the tales of Norse heroes and American frontiersmen by the hour. These books spurred his remarkable imagination so that he could hold Elliott, Anna and Corrine spellbound with the stories he made up. His original stories were usually about animals.

Theodore loved animals — his own Shetland pony he rode out in the country during summer vacations — the dogs, peacocks, cow and monkey next door at Uncle Bob's — all animals appealed to Theodore. He didn't think of them as pets only, he had a "scientific" curiosity about them which led him into the serious studies of a naturalist. This may have begun the morning he passed the market on Broadway, to which he was often sent for breakfast strawberries, and noticed a strange addition to the market display. There on a counter by itself lay a dead seal which had been caught in the harbor.

"That seal is exactly what I want," Theodore said to himself. Probably a dead seal in the house scarcely seemed appropriate to Mrs. Roosevelt, sweet and gracious as she was and quick to indulge the children's interests. Theodore was not permitted to buy the seal for "stuffing." That didn't discourage him from returning to the market to examine it day after day. He even managed to measure it and carefully recorded the figures in a notebook. Finally, he persuaded the owner of the market to give him the skull of the seal when it was taken off exhibition. Mrs. Roosevelt did not object to the skull, and it was used to start a collection which Theodore and his cousins called the "Roosevelt Museum of Natural History."

When Theodore's father found out about this passion for the study of mammals, he gave his son a little book by J. G. Wood, who was famous at the time for his popular books on natural history. Although he didn't realize it, Theodore was at a serious disadvantage in his study of nature. As he, himself, wrote later, "I was very near-sighted, so that the only things I could study were those I ran against or stumbled over." Of course, when the near-sightedness was discovered, he was fitted with glasses that corrected the handicap. (And the look that many people described later as fierce may have been simply the result of his limited vision.)

Just as the "Roosevelt Museum of Natural History" began to get attention, its exhibits swelling the bookcase in the back hall upstairs, Theodore's father announced that they were all going off to Europe for a year. Some ten-year-old boys would be delirious with such a prospect. Not Theodore. He was homesick during the entire trip, and described some of the choice European tourist attractions as "orful." One happy event he recorded. It was a Sunday of hiking in the woods with his father. Being devout in the Dutch Reformed faith, Mr. Roosevelt conducted an informal Sunday school for the children among the trees and wildflowers. Theodore wished church could always be that pleasant. But, mostly, he was bored with Europe. The Art galleries were stuffy places, Westminster Abbey and all of the dozens of other cathedrals did not compare in his mind with the familiar places at home in New York City. And so, while his parents tried to see to it that he had a "sociable time," he was gloomy with longing for home, and no one was as happy as Theodore when the family sailed back to the United States that May of 1870.

5

Observing animals and fish and insects absorbed more and more of Theodore's time. He was still keeping up with lessons assigned by the tutor, and he was following a rigorous regimen of exercise in the gymnasium. In fact, he was now taking lessons in boxing from an ex-prizefighter, John Long. But nothing compared with studying the specimens he constantly brought home.

To encourage this bent, Theodore's father and mother decided to let him take lessons in taxidermy from a Mr. Bell. From the very beginning, Theodore felt at home in Mr. Bell's small shop crammed with skillfully preserved models of his precise art. The tall, straight-backed taxidermist recognized at once the serious intentions of his pupil. They went beyond mere boyish curiosity. Still skinny and limited physically, Theodore had the mental power of total concentration. He listened raptly to everything Mr. Bell taught him and became a diligent observer. From this shared interest in nature, a lasting friendship grew which turned every lesson into a comfortable, happy encounter.

With only a quick knock, Theodore would push open the door and bounce into the shop, asking questions before even saying hello.

"Were you able to find a jay for us to work on, Mr. Bell?" The enthusiasm and anticipation of the boy never failed to please the taxidermist. "Yes, Ted. Look here — have you ever seen a prettier one?"

"Can't say that I have, Mr. Bell, but every jay I see always seems prettier than the last one."

"It's that blue — azure — azure like a winter sky."

The boy hung up his jacket and took his place beside his teacher at the long table. "Funny how jays can be so showy and hide the way they do in a tree." Mr. Bell's white head bent close to Theodore's sandy head over the dead bluejay. "It's fresh and clean, isn't it, Mr. Bell?"

"Yes, a fine specimen." The taxidermist placed the bird on its back once he had plugged the nostrils and throat with tow, a coarse flax used for stuffing. Theodore laid out the tools in perfect order. Knives as sharp as his father's straight razor, cutting pliers, needles and thread, scissors, crooked awls. These were important, but so were the tools of your mind, patience and perseverance. If you hurried, you could ruin the feathers. Cleaning them was an exacting process.

Theodore rubbed the wings of the jay lightly with a bit of wadding soaked in benzoline. Not one step can be hurried, he thought. I am more patient than when we began, that's for sure. And I've learned to handle the preserving compound carefully.

Mr. Bell made his own "soap" and kept it in small pots. "This is a potent mixture, Ted. Watch how I use it, and you won't be getting brittle nails or sore fingers."

"What's in it?" Theodore asked.

"Oh, lime and arsenic and camphor, among other things."

Soon Theodore could mix the compound himself. And he could clean a specimen as expertly as Mr. Bell. The scissors were steady in the old man's hand. "What is the thing to remember at this step, Ted?"

"The incision is made under the wing, not on the breast."

"Correct. Which wing? Where shall we begin?"

"The right one, sir. The damaged side." At each step

in the procedure Mr. Bell checked with his student, and Theodore knew his answers were correct.

Sometimes they would rest a few minutes, then he would look through the great morocco-bound books that were Mr. Bell's most cherished possessions: *Birds of America* in four volumes by John James Audubon. Mr. Bell had been a guide and companion to Audubon. He knew the years of study that went into those books. He also knew every detail in the magnificent life size pictures.

"If I learned anything from Mr. Audubon, Ted, it was thoroughness. Just study his notes and they'll show you what I mean. He never changed in that respect either." The old taxidermist looked away into the distance. "After he bought his place over here on the Hudson, I used to sit with him on the front porch and look up and down the river. You wouldn't believe the details he'd notice as the birds flew by. He never stopped discovering. Yes, sir, Mr. Audubon was thorough."

Whether listening to his teacher reminisce or working with him on a project, Theodore looked forward to those afternoons in the taxidermist's shop. It was as much fun as being alone. And he did like to be alone in the woods where he watched birds for hours without budging. The shop and the woods were his favorite places.

6

On Sunday evenings the Roosevelt children gathered with their parents in the front parlor. It was not used otherwise unless there was a party. The family made much of this pleasant time after a day of church-going. Not that church services were unpleasant, but Theodore, especially, found it trying to keep his "best clothes" clean and neat for such long, long hours.

One Sunday evening he was absent-mindedly counting the glass prisms on the grand gas chandelier that hung in the parlor. He had counted them a thousand times before, and the same thing always happened. He would forget with which prism he began the count. There! It happened again. All of the shimmering, turning prisms looked alike. He started counting again, paying no attention to the conversation between his father and mother, but on the count of sixteen, he heard his father say, "President Grant has asked me to accept an appointment to represent our government at the World's Exposition next year."

"The great 1873 World's Exposition in Vienna the papers are already advertising?"

"Yes, my dear. How would you like your husband to be the commissioner for the United States?" Mr. Roosevelt smiled teasingly.

"I think it's an honor and I'm proud of you." A look of tenderness passed between the two adults.

"If we left this fall, we could spend the year traveling. Don't you think it's time for the children to see more of the world?"

"Yes, and the New York winters are so harmful to Theodore," Mrs. Roosevelt said.

"I was thinking of that too. Maybe a winter in Egypt would be beneficial for the boy. It's mild and sunny there, and I've inquired about cruises up the Nile."

That settles it, Theodore said to himself. That trip abroad four years ago was a dreadful bore, but maybe this one will be better. I'd like to see Alexandria. It must be an ideal site if Alexander the Great picked it out. And when we go to see the pyramids Elliott and I can ride camels. I can hunt new specimens along the Nile too. I might find something exotic no one has ever recorded. You never can tell.

When the Roosevelts landed in Alexandria several weeks later, Theodore was loaded down with equipment, including his gun for hunting specimens and taxidermy supplies for preserving them. One of the first things he did upon arriving in Egypt was to buy a book by an English clergyman who had made the trip up the Nile and had written his observations of the birds he saw along its banks. The book helped Theodore identify birds that would have been nameless otherwise. And he was careful to learn both the English and Latin names.

For two months the big sailing vessel Mr. Roosevelt had hired, took the family up the quiet river, making stops along its banks to let the children explore as much as they liked. Theodore kept the donkeys and guides busy on these trips into the countryside. Every night he returned to the boat with wild life to "stuff"; every night the collection added to the general disarray of his and Elliott's cabin. It was growing, as was Theodore, at an astounding rate. The stink of arsenical soap and dead birds in various stages of preservation became too much

for Elliott; he demanded a cabin alone. He refused to share his brother's "laboratory" for one more mile!

As the Roosevelts had hoped, the climate was good for Theodore's asthma. Suddenly his trousers looked shrunken, and he could no longer button his jacket. By the time the river trip ended in Cairo, he had to get new outfits before going on to the Holy Land, Syria, Greece and Turkey.

From Algiers Mr. Roosevelt left for Vienna; Mrs. Roosevelt went to Carlsbad for a rest; the children were taken to Dresden where they boarded with Dr. Minckwitz and his family. The summer in Dresden was a happy one for Theodore. He learned to read and speak German. He decided he liked German poetry as much as he liked English poetry. On walks taken into the country an old artist taught him to sketch what he saw. He observed the citizens of Dresden daily and came to admire their industriousness, love of learning, national pride and affection. Of course, he was still collecting, which kept the Minckwitz household on the alert as they were forever opening drawers and cabinet doors to find dead snakes and hedgehogs and moles.

When the Roosevelts returned to New York in the fall of 1873, Theodore was fifteen. He had changed and developed beyond his parents' hopes, and, although he was still physically below par, his health was better than it had ever been; his mind was keen and quick; he could concentrate with amazing determination; his humor was unrestrained. His cousin Maude thought he was "very amusing" even though, in her opinion, he had a superiority complex.

It was time to make decisions about the future, specifically about Theodore's education. In some subjects he read avidly and was advanced. In those he did not like, his lack of formal schooling really handicapped him. To enter Harvard, he must know Latin and Greek and Math as well as he knew Science and History. To remedy this imbalance he began serious studies with Arthur H. Cutler who later founded a well-known prep school. *private 1t.*

In addition to studies, there were boxing lessons (Theodore won a pewter mug in the lightweight class and bragged about it for years), the usual natural history pursuits, and trips to Oyster Bay where he rowed his own boat in all kinds of weather, fighting the wind and rough water on stormy days, racing the clouds and sails on clear ones.

By the time he was seventeen he was a good runner as well as boxer, and had enough stamina to compete in the broad jump and pole vaulting contests. In his diary he noted:

height ....5 feet, eight inches
weight ....124 lbs.
chest expansion ....34 inches

His body was catching up with his mind at last. And the same absolute concentration he had practiced in taxidermy made it possible for him to do three years of study in two so that by the fall of 1876 he passed the entrance exams to become one of the "Harvard men."

7

American universities today are so huge they are sometimes complete cities within themselves. Harvard, when Theodore entered, was scarcely larger than its now famous Yard. The town surrounding it, Cambridge, Massachusetts, was dull and sleepy. For excitement, Harvard students took a horse-drawn car to Boston where they gathered at the Parker House. In winter the cars were without heat. The straw covered floors soon smelled of wet snow and tobacco juice. On these trips to Boston, Theodore stood out sharply from his classmates just as he did on campus. Not because he was popular, rather because he was utterly different from the other fellows. Most Harvard men affected a casual slouch when they walked — they sauntered — it wasn't good form to move quickly. Theodore went on a trot. In the same way, it was considered "narrow-minded to excel"; Theodore studied ambitiously and drove the professors to exasperation by demanding reasons for the theories they taught. Other students drank and smoked and discussed girls for recreation; Theodore neither drank nor smoked and considered tea with a pal, or a small opera party great fun. He was a thorough-going nonconformist without being aware of it.

A short time before, he had been pale, timid and nervous—indifferent about his dress, awkward and bumptious in his manner. Now he wore stylish "sideboard" whiskers and the fashions in vogue. His classmates accused him of being an exhibitionist and called him a dandy.

Still another difference set him apart. The damp first floor rooms at the school were unhealthy, at least for one of his uncertain resistance. And so he had private rooms at No. 16 Winthrop Street which ran halfway between the school and the Charles River. This made it possible for Theodore to read all he wanted to and to surround himself with the usual disorder of his natural history collections. While it is doubtful that he missed the constant companionships of dormitory life, he did miss his family and wrote to them regularly. He wrote about his love and affection for his parents and his brother and sisters in a most unself-conscious way. If this was considered "mushy" in a college boy, it must have been in a man of importance as well, because he never changed. He was always tender and demonstrative toward those he loved.

Such eccentricities would have isolated young Roosevelt from his fellows had it not been for his social background. As it was, he "made" Porcellian, Hasty Pudding, O. K., Alpha Delta Phi, Dickey, and the Institute of 1770. This meant his friends were of the "club set," New Yorkers and Bostonians of social position.

He also continued his athletic activities. By now it was clear that he would never be a champion, just as it was clear he had no real intellectual genius, but this only made him try harder. He was courageous. He was wholehearted. He was disciplined. It is remarkable that the New York *Times* described one of his college boxing matches as "almost professional," and in his senior year at Harvard he was awarded a Phi Beta Kappa key.

All the Roosevelts believed in practical witness to their traditional religious faith. Theodore's father was prominent in charitable causes and taught a Sunday school class in a slum mission. It was perfectly natural

28

for Theodore to do the same, although he did not start out in a mission. His first Sunday school class was at Christ Church Episcopal in Cambridge. Everything was going along splendidly, he thought, until the rector stopped him one Sunday morning.

"I hear you have a boy in your class who has a black eye, Mr. Roosevelt." The rector seemed pleasantly interested.

"Yes, sir, that's true," Theodore said. "It's black and several other colors. He got it in a just fight, so he ought to be proud of it."

"A just fight?" the rector asked slyly.

"Yes, sir. You see, a neighborhood bully pinched this boy's little sister, so he beat up the bully."

"And you gave him a dollar for his reward. Is that correct?"

"Yes, sir, I did." Theodore smiled broadly. The rector did not smile. His expression was suddenly stern and disapproving.

"I didn't believe the report when it came to me, but now I see it's quite true. I must warn you, young man, you are not to use the church's precious time promoting fights!"

That wasn't all. When the rector learned that Theodore was of the Dutch Reformed denomination, he ordered him to become an Episcopalian. With the courtesy of a true Christian gentleman, Theodore responded by giving the rector a hearty handshake, then saying, "This I refuse to do." His tone of voice was firm but kind. "I see no reason for it. I shall find a class to teach in a mission where the clergyman will not be so intolerant."

And he did.

8

One thing in particular disappointed Theodore Roosevelt in his college studies. His chief interests were still scientific, and he had taken for granted that Harvard offered the best courses in the field. He was surprised to find that any kind of research carried on outside the laboratory was not recognized by the school.

"My taste was specialized in a totally different direction," he later wrote. "I had no more desire nor ability to be a microscopist and section-cutter than to be a mathematician."

His father had warned, "If you are going to have a career as a naturalist, you will have to give up the luxuries that go with money-making in a successful business."

"Would you rather I went into business, Father?" Theodore asked.

"No, I prefer that you do the thing that gives you the most satisfaction. If that's in the field of science, then I shall help you financially, because it will never pay you enough for a good living."

"I'm serious about science. I'm sure of that," Theodore said.

"Then I want you to do the very best work that's in you. It must not be simply the hobby of a rich man's son."

Theodore thought a lot about what his father said. Especially during his second year at Harvard, the year his father died. By the third year he had changed his mind about becoming a scientist. The loss of his father had been a severe blow. It made him uncertain about many things, but it also made him more determined to be respected for what he made of himself.

Some people may have expected him to become a playboy because he was financially independent. If they did, they were fooled. Just the way Bill Sewall was fooled. The first time he saw Theodore he figured he was a tenderfoot from the big city. Bill was one of the finest hunting and fishing guides in Aroostook County, Maine. Once Theodore's cousins introduced him to Bill, he began making a couple of trips a year to Maine, a welcome change from the Harvard routine. The young man and the wise, weather-toughened trapper soon became great friends. Bill was tall and muscular, cunning as a coon, strong as a bear. His physique and high ideals were similar to those of Theodore's father, and that made it easy for Theodore to feel comfortable with the woodsman, in spite of their contrasting backgrounds.

At first, Bill tested Theodore's endurance, figuring he probably couldn't "take much." In no time at all it became clear that Theodore would hike until he dropped rather than admit he was tired. A 25-mile hike was just another kind of challenge.

One day they set out to climb Mount Katahdin, the highest mountain in Maine. As they crossed a stream, Theodore lost a shoe in the swift current. He hadn't brought along another pair, but he did have some thin-soled moccasins. He put them on and climbed the mountain. All the way up, Bill knew the stones were bruising and cutting Theodore's feet, but he also knew that Theodore would "never let on." No wonder Bill took a fancy to him. In the winter the two friends strapped on their snowshoes and stalked game through the woods. They

31

visited loggers in their camps, and Theodore won his way with these rough workmen in spite of his youth.

If the topic of conversation was something Theodore knew little about, he kept quiet. If he was informed on a controversial subject, he would jump into the discussion with both feet, frequently winning his companions to his point of view. Bill liked that. He was proud of Theodore.

One night a man in their camp remarked, "I always treat a fellow as though he was a rascal 'til I find out different."

"That's not giving him much of a chance, is it?" Theodore asked. "I prefer it the other way 'round — I figure every man is honest until he proves to me he isn't."

Bill Sewall grinned at Theodore. That was the way he looked at it too. The young man was educated all right, but better than that, he had an uncommon amount of common sense.

9

It was October, 1878. Theodore was a junior at Harvard, and in another week he would be twenty. Several times he changed the tilt of his hat as he finished dressing for a party at the home of Richard Saltonstall. Richard was one of his closest friends. Upon arriving at the party, Theodore looked around and thought everyone there was familiar to him. But he hadn't noticed the new girl until Richard said, "Come over to the piano and meet my cousin." As soon as they started walking toward the young lady, Theodore decided she was the most fashionable and the most beautiful of all the guests.

"Alice, may I present Theodore Roosevelt? I've been telling you about him. Teddy, this is Miss Alice Lee."

Suddenly, for Theodore, there was no one else in the room. "I loved her as soon as I saw her sweet, fair young face . . . ." he wrote later. Even though she was only seventeen, Alice's grace and lack of self-consciousness made her seem mature for her years. And she *was* beautiful. Her hair was fair, her eyes blue and wide apart; her nose tilted a bit, her mouth delicate and expressive.

To Alice, Theodore was just another beau, but she underestimated his determination. He wangled weekend invitations to the Saltonstall home on Chestnut Hill and courted her with all of the vigor he had formerly spent on childhood enthusiasms. She was definitely not impressed with his rapid-fire talk about the snakes and bugs and turtles he kept in his rooms. Nor could she feel anything resembling interest when he demanded she watch from the balcony of the gymnasium while he fought for the lightweight boxing championship. His energy and vitality overwhelmed her, which may have been why she continued to discourage him. Being rebuffed plunged Theodore into such a black mood he would go off alone, refusing to talk to anyone. For days no one knew where he was. When Alice heard about this, she realized that his vivacious, assured manner concealed a rare sensitivity deep inside.

It was a stormy courtship, and by the time Alice and her mother spent Christmas of 1879 with Theodore's family at Oyster Bay, he was a possessive suitor. At Harvard, it became obvious that he was hopelessly in love. He forgot writing assignments on the *Advocate,* neglected his natural science activities, found it impossible to concentrate on lectures and reading. If for any reason the word love was mentioned he blushed furiously. Even Alice's eventual promise to marry him did not relieve his jealousy or his anxiety, and the wonder is that he managed to graduate. But on June 30, 1880, he received the Bachelor of Arts degree from Harvard University.

Possibly Alice found it too exhausting to plan the wedding with Theodore under foot, because by summer he was off on a hunting trip in Minnesota with his brother Elliot, writing ardent letters every day. No matter how much he enjoyed the outdoor life, it seemed like the longest summer of his life.

At last, on his twenty-second birthday, October 27, 1880, he married the lovely Alice in the First Parish Church of Brookline, Massachusetts.

The honeymoon was postponed and the couple moved to New York City to share the home of Theodore's mother. Happily, she adored Alice who had a grace and charm resembling her own. At least that was what Theodore thought — the highest compliment he could pay his bride.

Having given up the idea of being a professor of science or a professional naturalist, he was faced with a decision about the future. True, he was financially independent; he could support Alice comfortably. But he would have to do more than occasionally work on the book he had begun in college, titled *The Naval War of 1812.* He must do something useful. He enrolled in Columbia Law School and studied in the law office of his Uncle Robert. The Law simply could not fire Theodore's exceptional imagination. To him it was dull and hopelessly boring.

He was relieved to get away from the office to take Alice to Europe that spring. They toured from the British Isles south to Switzerland, and as you would expect, he climbed the Matterhorn, thoroughly enjoying the danger of the expedition.

He planned to continue his law studies when they returned to New York. Instead, Theodore Roosevelt was abruptly thrust into politics. He had joined the Republican Association in his district, the 21st, because he thought people of his social standing should be more active in public affairs. This contrasted sharply with the views of most gentlemen from his background who insisted that politics was too dirty, "too low down" for their participation. Theodore was convinced that politics had descended to a corrupt level for that very reason. Men of character and influence were refusing to take their responsibility.

And so family friends ridiculed Theodore for attending the meetings of the 21st district every month in Morton Hall, a huge, dingy room above a saloon, furnished with benches and spittoons. Morton Hall was not a respectable place, in the opinion of some New Yorkers, but opinions mattered little to young Roosevelt. By going to the hall every time politicians gathered, he learned to speak their language. The way he had learned the language of Mr. Bell and Bill Sewall and the Maine loggers. He soon learned, too, which of the men were ordinary "heelers," and which were leaders. Jake Hess ran the machine in the 21st with the help of hundreds of captains. One of these captains was Joe Murray.

Theodore liked Joe. He decided Joe was a man of courage and loyalty. More important, he was honest. The only other thing the two men had in common was a love of fine horses. Joe said he had been reared a barefoot Irish immigrant on the sidewalks of First Avenue, but he had risen to enough success now to own a first class trotter. He would take Theodore driving, which established a genuine friendship, since Theodore admired the horse as much as the owner. Still, he was surprised when Joe and his cronies chose him, a "silk stocking," to be their candidate for the state Assembly, the lower house of the New York Legislature.

Energetically beginning his first campaign tour of the district, Theodore was introduced by Joe to an important saloon keeper, who looked the boyish stranger up and down before asking, "Are you prepared to treat the liquor business fairly, Mr. Roosevelt?"

"Yes, sir," Theodore said, ignoring the threatening tone in the man's voice. "Yes sir, I intend to treat *all* interests fairly."

That obviously was not the answer the saloon keeper expected. "And what will you do about the sky-rocketing prices of our liquor licenses?"

Without hesitating, Theodore said, "I don't think

they're high enough, sir. I'll do everything in my power to raise them!"

Joe Murray grabbed his friend Roosevelt by the arm and pushed him out the door of the saloon, explaining to the would-be politician that he might do better on Fifth Avenue with people of his own class; the old hands would do the electioneering on Sixth.

In spite of this shaky beginning, Theodore won the nomination. Joe's backing took care of that. And young Roosevelt's future was decided for him.

10

At twenty-four, Theodore was the youngest legislator in the Albany Assembly that January of 1882. He was also a Republican in an Assembly dominated by Democrats. That mattered little in state politics, according to his later writings. "My friendships were made not with regard to party lines," he wrote, "but because I found, and my friends found, that we had the same convictions on questions of principle and questions of policy."

This explains why Theodore's best friend during his stay in Albany was Billy O'Neill. Billy had kept a small country store; Theodore was from the largest city in America. In ancestry and background they could not have been more unlike, but in principle and policy they agreed; both believed in a powerful national government *and* in Lincoln's concepts of the rights of the people.

Before Roosevelt had participated in many Assembly debates everyone knew he held these beliefs. Some legislators pretended his ideas were contradictory, others dubbed them unrealistic, the dream of a very young reformer. One thing was certain, no one intimidated Theodore Roosevelt. He fought the "special interests" of big business as though he thought all freshmen assemblymen did that. Of course, they didn't at all; from the very start he was an exception.

It was difficult for him to speak in public at first. His knees shook and he stammered from nervousness. He wished he had studied elocution at college! If his ideas were to be heard, though, he would have to do the talking, so, in his decisive way he overcame his fears, thought out carefully what to say in advance, and with much practice became a forceful speaker.

Alice was often one of the guests in the Assembly Chamber who applauded him.

Before long it was evident that Theodore was on the opposite side from "the black horse cavalry" (a name given those who paid bribes to have their interests protected), "the timid good men" and "the dull, conservative men." These three types would always arouse Roosevelt's wrath. And he would certainly arouse theirs.

In one case, involving a Judge Westbrook who had been "bought off" in a fraudulent bankruptcy case, Theodore led a revolt against the indifferent majority. They were shocked into listening when he demanded that the judge be impeached. Some thirty to forty assemblymen backed this proposal, and the battle began in earnest. Seemingly it ended in defeat for the young reformer because the judge was "whitewashed," and the charges against him dismissed. But the newspapers gave the case steady coverage. One day Roosevelt was merely a new name in the Assembly. The next, Roosevelt was a name known all over the United States.

The old professionals were not impressed by headlines. They said a reformer didn't have a political chance, but this reformer went on to prove them wrong by winning his seat again in the next session. His margin of 2,000 votes was larger than it had been the first time. And he won that margin in spite of the landslide election of Grover Cleveland, the Democratic candidate for Governor.

By the year 1884, Roosevelt was an important leader champion for justice, and the most promising Republican in the New York Assembly. He was widely considered a "winner."

On weekends he hurried to his mother's home in

New York City to see her and Alice. To tell them what had been accomplished since the last visit. And he talked and dreamed with his beloved wife about their child who was to be born that February.

The afternoon the announcement reached him that he had become a father, all of his Assembly colleagues congratulated him and sent him off to the train in high spirits. The trip from Albany to New York City seemed endless. He reached his mother's house at midnight, eager and jubilant, but when his brother Elliot opened the door, he knew something was wrong.

"Your daughter was born last night, Theodore, and all went well until today. Our mother has been stricken. She is dying. And so is Alice. There is a curse on this house!"

Elliot's bitter words thundered in Theodore's ears as he rushed up the stairs to the third floor. He found Alice asleep.

"Alice, dearest, I'm here . . . it's Theodore . . . Alice . . . " She didn't even open her eyes. In agony he sat down on the bed and cradled her in his arms. And he did not leave her except for a few moments in the early morning when he was called to his mother's room. There was nothing he could do. Helplessly he watched his mother die, and broken-hearted, he returned to Alice. The following afternoon, she, too, died. He was still holding her.

Within eleven stark, unbelievable hours, the joy and truth of loving were blotted out. Without warning, typhoid fever had claimed his mother, Bright's disease, his wife. Darkness closed over him. Death, the old enemy he had wrestled through the illnesses of his own childhood, had defeated him in a way he had not dreamed of. And he, Theodore Roosevelt, the winner, *was* defeated.

41

11

The following day, February 15, 1885, a resolution of condolence was adopted by the assembly, and out of respect for a fellow member, the legislature of New York adjourned.

On the 20th, Theodore returned to his work in Albany and remained to the end of the session, but a "light had gone out." He was existing on sheer courage. The grief in his face kept anyone from mentioning Alice. There is no record that he ever did.

Desperately he needed to be alone — away from the world of politics — away from the sea of sympathy that surrounded him. And so he went from the Republican convention in Chicago that summer west to South Dakota, to the Bad Lands.

The year before, he had made his first trip west to join a couple of ranchers in a cattle venture at a place called Chimney Butte. Chimney Butte ranch was his destination once more. Maybe he could find peace in that desolate place. Twenty miles down the river he owned another ranch, Elkhorn. His partners, Ferris and Merrifield, met the train when it pulled in and took him to Chimney Butte. They had readied a small cabin which would give Roosevelt the privacy he needed.

It was June, the cottonwood thickets were gray-green. He listened to the songs of the hermit thrush, the brown thrasher, the Missouri skylark. The beauty of the vast open spaces began to rest and heal him; living in the saddle from sunup to dark, the strenuous work of rounding up cattle and hunting for fresh meat supplies hardened and developed his body. The way Theodore described it: "It was a fine healthy life; it taught a man self-reliance, hardihood, and the value of instant decision. . . ."

This was a time in American history when courtesy and good manners were rare out west. It was inevitable that the would-be-cowboy was jeered for the way he combed his hair, for his fancy glasses, the way he said "r-a-w-t-h-a." His grammar was too precise and his voice pitched too high for the "natives" to take him seriously.

There's a story that the first time he rode in a round-up, the seasoned cowhands almost fell to the ground laughing when they heard Theodore yell in his thin voice, "Hasten forward quickly there!"

They didn't laugh long. A crack roper said to his buddies one day, soon after Theodore's arrival at the ranch, "Who'll lay a bet with me that Roosevelt can tame that new bronc over there?"

"Four-Eyes?" another hand said scornfully. "He can't see to rope a post! He won't stay on that bronc ten seconds dressed up in them fancy duds without somethin' rippin' wide open."

The group of men lounging along the corral fence guffawed. Theodore didn't know he was the object of their joke — or bet. He did look out of place in expensive sombrero, decorated chaps, embroidered fringed shirt. As he walked toward the men, the silver spurs on his boots jangled. He was a colorful if comical sight.

"Go on an' ask him, Pete," a lean old cowpoke drawled. "If he agrees to ride, I'll bet on him stickin' in the saddle . . . just for sport."

At twenty-five the dashing greenhorn from back east was ready for anything; he accepted the challenge to mount the bronc without hesitating. Even the bronc

seemed insulted and broke immediately into a breakneck gallop that sent Theodore's fancy hat sailing. Then
the bronc stopped, all four legs rigid, braking, sliding,
skidding in the feathery dust. The rider leaned back and
hugged the sides of the bronc still tighter with his knees.
That started the bronc bucking — up and down — twist-
ing and kicking.

"You said he couldn't stay on longer'n ten seconds,
Pete," the old cowpoke said. "Looks like yer miscalcu-
lated, don't it?"

"Just wait," Pete said. "There goes the dude's spectacles! That'll fix him."

The bronc and Theodore were struggling now with
all their might — horse strength against male stubborn-
ness. The men were not grinning anymore. Whoever
won or lost this contest deserved respect.

Theodore, his eyes squinted shut, teeth clenched,
came down hard in the saddle with a great slap as the
bronc plunged straight into the air — then down — forward — backward — up — down, and with one final powerful leap pitched the rider over his head into a mulberry
bush.

Bets were forgotten as the cowhands rushed forward to help Theodore to his feet. The one called Pete
said slowly, "I didn't think you could stick it, boss. You
were on him for three minutes at least!"

Theodore brushed at the fringed shirt and picked up
his steel-rimmed spectacles. "You saw me go leather,
though," he said in disgust. It was a greater disgrace
"to go leather," which meant to hold on by grabbing the
saddlehorn, than it was to be thrown. Theodore was disappointed in himself!

That kind of fortitude won him the friendship of the
punchers. He was one of them. With characteristic

45

eagerness, he learned to drive cattle and brand steers. This was a man's work, and he became as tough as the rest. He gained weight, grew a thick mustache, and won the final victory over asthma.

In his own opinion he was never more than a "respectable" rider, but he learned to handle every kind of horse. He wasn't a perfect marksman either, but he could outlast his peers trailing wild game. Some men are born with quick hands and eyes. Theodore had neither; he considered his abilities very ordinary. But he developed them by resolute practice. Nerve and control were gained the same way. If he was afraid ("stricken with buck fever"), and he admitted he was afraid of wild broncs and wild gunmen, he didn't show it. He acted without panic, and the act was so convincing his "ordinary" abilities seemed superior to onlookers.

To help run the cattle business, Roosevelt invited his old friend, Bill Sewall, to join him in the Bad Lands. Bill accepted the offer and brought along his nephew. The three men built a house on the Elkhorn ranch which Theodore enjoyed for the remainder of his stay there. It was a long house, low, with a big front porch. He had a bedroom to himself, and he had a rocking chair. "I am very fond of rocking chairs," he said. Then there were also the luxuries of favorite books to read and a rubber bathtub.

When the bitter cold swept down from Canada, a fire roared in the living room fireplace and buffalo robes were piled onto the beds. Deer, antelope and ducks were plentiful for meat. There was even milk after a few cows were tamed. It was a rugged life, but Theodore shared every hardship cheerfully, without complaint.

He was at home with all sorts of men; his reputation for hard work and honesty spread across the Bad Lands.

In 1885 he had been appointed deputy sheriff of Billings County; he tracked down and captured thieves; he organized an association of cattlemen to insure enforcement of the law.

Christmases were spent in the East with little Alice who lived with his sister Corrine's family. On those visits to New York, he saw many old friends, but there was one who became more important than the others. Edith Kermit Carow, one of Corrine's best friends, had been a childhood playmate, having lived near Grandfather Roosevelt on Fourteenth Street in New York. Three years younger than Theodore, she knew just how to let him be himself. She knew he was as sensitive as he was impetuous, as tender as he was vigorous.

Back at the Elkhorn after the holidays, he wrote long letters to Edith, and by November of 1886 had persuaded her to marry him. Time and the silence "under the vast empty sky" had mended his broken heart. It was a beautiful kind of loneliness he felt as he sat on the veranda watching black vultures cast shadows on the sun-struck river bed which lay down the slope from the ranch house. The melancholy cooing of the mourning doves did not make him sad anymore. Even though the western experiment was a financial failure, it had served its purpose. He could return to his old home and activities. He would begin again, and there would be Edith to help him.

12

Another interest, aside from Edith and little Alice, drew Theodore Roosevelt to New York once more. Politics. He was asked to run for mayor. He ran — and lost. Some of the party leaders said he was too young to be trusted with such an important office, and that may have been the reason for his defeat. But it was a resounding defeat and a political obituary was published in a British paper predicting he was through as a Republican figure. It flatly stated that he was not "Presidential timber."

Theodore may not have noticed his critics very much because he was thinking of more pleasant things; that December of 1886, he and Edith were married in London and spent two happy months honeymooning on the Continent.

A home was waiting for them when they landed back in the States, a huge rambling house called Sagamore Hill which overlooked Oyster Bay. In contrast to his new happiness, Theodore's financial affairs out west were on the brink of disaster. It was necessary for him to go at once to the ranch to check losses. The winter in the Bad Lands had been so ferocious, tens of thousands of cattle had died. In fact, few living things remained. Scores of men lost their lives in the blizzards, and Roosevelt's ranch investments, amounting to over a third of his inheritance, were totally wiped out. By the summer of 1887 he had sold off the remnants of his herds and ended the western venture.

PART TWO
1886 - 1901

13

April was only a few days away, but the wind off the Sound was sharp and moist. The fields were still brown, the trees gray. Edith didn't mind. The sky was a clear blue, the choppy waters of Oyster Bay deep green. Blue and brown — gray and green — hummed the high wheels of the carriage. Spring was on the way, and Edith had never been more excited about its coming. But then this would be her first spring in a home of her own — the wife of Theodore Roosevelt.

She glanced at him sitting erect beside her, his hands quiet and sure with the reins. The profile was handsome. Rimless glasses on a black silk cord gave him a false air of arrogance. He does have the most haughty forehead, Edith thought to herself. And the close style of haircut makes him look mature. I'm glad he got rid of those ridiculous side whiskers he wore at college and the waves in his hair. She looked again to the pastures alongside the road. The horses slowed to a walk. They were climbing now.

This would not be her first visit to Sagamore Hill. A memory stirred uneasily at the edge of her happiness. The house was first named "Leehom" for Alice Lee. It was a wonder he had gone on to build it. He and Alice had planned the house together, and two weeks after her death, he told the contractor to begin building. While he was living in the West, it was completed, and he asked his sister Anna to move from New York City to become Sagamore's first hostess. From that time till this past winter, its twenty rooms had spilled over with servants and relatives and house-party guests. Edith had been invited by Anna to a hunt ball. That was over a year ago. She had been driven up the hill road, this same road, to the wide roofed portico that extended over the driveway allowing one to alight and enter protected from the weather.

Anna was vivacious and hospitable like her brother, Theodore. They liked nothing better than to get people together for lively conversation around a table set for fifty. I'll never compare with Anna, Edith thought, I'm too reserved to be a good hostess. He knows that about me, though. I wonder what he's thinking. He hasn't said a word since we started up the hill.

The carriage turned to the left, and there it was, dignified and solid looking in spite of the mixture of shingles and bricks, gables and dormers, porches and porticos.

"Home at last, Edith," Theodore sighed with happy relief and placed his hand over hers. The warmth of it penetrated her gloves, the pressure of it tender and loving. "Sagamore Hill," he said proudly. "I named it for old Sagamore Mohannis, the Indian Chief who signed away rights to this land 250 years ago. I've roamed these fields and climbed the slopes since I was fifteen. This place means more to me than any other spot on earth. And for a long time I've waited for this moment, when I could bring you here to stay."

The horses stopped at the side entrance. Theodore jumped to the ground and ran around the carriage. "Welcome, your ladyship," he said, laughing up at Edith, offering his hand. She stepped down, his arms went round her, and they stood together under the wide roof of the portico. There were no maids in starched aprons to greet them. The house had been closed for the winter.

Theodore fitted the key in the lock and turned it. The great oak door swung open, and they walked into the paneled hall which was the way Edith remembered it, except for all of those white sheets protecting the furnishings and wild game trophies from dust.

Could it have been only twenty-four hours ago that they had arrived at Anna's, following the tiresome ocean crossing? Down the curving stairway of Anna's New York house had come Alice, Theodore's three-year-old. Alice looked like a round-eyed princess in her best dress with its elegant sash. In her arms she carried a huge bouquet of pink roses for her new mother. Once they were presented, the little girl flung herself at her father and kissed him until she was out of breath.

Soon we will bring Alice here to Sagamore Hill, Edith thought. I wonder if she will like it the way her father does. I must hire enough servants to help me care for her and this house. My, the decorating is stuffy! The furniture we selected in Europe will certainly be an improvement. But what *will* I do with twelve bedrooms?

By summer, Edith knew why there were so many bedrooms. New York was a mere thirty miles away, and the railroad was nearby. Guests arrived and departed constantly. Neighbors and relatives dropped in for tea and tennis. Always Theodore talked; talked about anything from wild flowers to tariffs. Edith listened. She liked people, and she had a gift for making them feel welcome in her home, but a few at a time would have been her preference.

This was just one of the adjustments she must make, if she was going to live with Theodore. They had known each other most of their lives. As children, they played together daily. As teen-aged young people, they had often dated. Their friends expected them to marry. But during the college years their interests broadened, taking them in different directions. Edith was admired at Miss Comstock's exclusive school. She was pretty, poised, independent. The other girls envied her wardrobe and the way she modeled it. At the same time, she seemed to care little for their feminine gossip or the flattering attentions of young gentlemen. This was mistaken by some people for aloofness. And wasn't it odd the way she went off with a book every time they discussed fashions?

Well, I haven't changed much, Edith thought, as she watched Theodore wave good-by to several carriage-loads of guests. This house is getting to be a hotel! I wish we could have a minute to ourselves.

As though he were reading her thoughts, Theodore turned to his wife and said, "Now, my dear, before anyone else comes, let's take a row over to Lloyd's Neck."

"That's a perfect idea," Edith said. "You select some books to take along while I make sandwiches." How sensitive of Theodore, she thought. I wonder if anyone else knows this side of him — the side that gives me such rest and peace. When we're alone, he forgets big issues and talks about the birds we hear, and reads aloud my favorite poetry. Or sometimes he doesn't say a word for hours, content just to be with me.

The outing they shared that day was typical of many they would have for the rest of their lives, no matter how busy or important they became. Theodore rowed energetically until they reached the opposite shore. They pulled the boat onto the sand and swinging the picnic basket between them, went in search of a shady locust tree. Barefoot and lazy, they spread a quilt and "plopped." They fed each other sandwiches of sweet butter and watercress. They laughed at the funny things

54

Alice had done that morning. They read to each other from the familiar books.

"Did you bring Matthew Arnold, darling?"

Theodore knew she would ask that. "Yes, but I don't need the book for your favorite lines — 'Ah, love, let us be true

> To one another! for the world, which seems
> To lie before us like a land of dreams,
> So various, so beautiful, so new . . .' "

His voice was low and soothing. These were the moments she treasured, when time stood still and only a wren or a grasshopper could interrupt them.

When he had finished reciting the poem, he kissed her fingers playfully and mused, "When our son is born four months from now, we will teach him our poems."

Edith laughed. "When he is old enough, we'll bring him here."

"Alice too?"

"Oh, yes — Alice too!"

14

On September 13, 1887, Theodore Junior was born. Alice described him as a "howling polly parrot." She would not permit the nurse to move her or her small rocking chair away from his crib. There was only happiness in the house on Sagamore Hill. This did not mean that Theodore Senior was not restless. Being a father took lots of time, but it did not take all of his time. He needed to be doing something in politics, trying out his reform ideas and serving the public.

Washington seemed to have forgotten him, though. And while he asked his good friend Henry Cabot Lodge, "Will you please remind the President of my availability?" no request came for his services. To have a project, he began writing a history of the territory between the Alleghenies and the Mississippi. He also wrote numerous articles for magazines about his ranching and hunting experiences. He worked on biographies of Thomas Hart Benton and Gouverneur Morris. He wrote as easily as he talked and in the same garrulous style. The effort may have absorbed him, but the critics judged his published materials superficial.

For two years Theodore wrote while, at the same time, keeping up with every development within the Republican party. Party leaders received letters of comment and criticism from him by the dozen. It was a period of change for the Republicans. Mark Hanna, the powerful Ohio politician, was promoting William McKinley to prominence in Congress, a sure sign that the Old Guard was giving way to the younger hopefuls. That may have influenced President Harrison to appoint Roosevelt to the United States Civil Service Commission, which was thought of as a relatively unimportant post since it paid $3,500.00 a year and controlled no political patronage.

That did not matter to Theodore. He accepted the appointment and left his family at Oyster Bay until a home could be found for them in the Capitol.

The Civil Service Commission was located at Eighth and "E" Streets. President Cleveland had tried to rid it of corruption but nothing had changed in the Commission, not for years. The very atmosphere of the office was doty and drab. And so on the morning of May 13, 1889, the Commission's secretary, Matthew Halloran, was decidedly unprepared for the arrival of Roosevelt who entered with the speed and force of a cyclone.

"I'm the new Commissioner," he announced. "Where is the telephone?" From that moment Halloran began making appointments, taking dictation, arranging conferences, without pause. The new boss paced up and down in front of the secretary's desk issuing orders, emphasizing points by smacking his right fist into his left hand. At times, Halloran missed a word or two of dictation as he wondered how in the world Roosevelt's glasses stayed in place.

Two goals were uppermost in the Commissioner's mind: he would administer the bureau efficiently, giving the taxpayers their "money's worth" and he would make Civil Service appointments on the basis of merit, which would soon eliminate the "spoils system." "To the victors belong the spoils," was a slogan of every party that got into power—not in so many words, but in practice. If the President was a Democrat, members of the opposite party were thrown out of office so that loyal Democratic politicians could enjoy the patronage they had been promised in case they won the elections. It was the same in the case of a Republican victory.

Patronage will always be a part of politics, but in the '80s it added up to corruption on a fearful scale. Could a challenge have been more custom-made for Roosevelt? He was daring and ready to fight, young enough to think that right was right, wrong was wrong, and he would prove it.

Immediately he was engaged in battle with everyone who stood in his way, and because he raised his voice louder than other reformers, he made headlines.

Such a young idealist was bound to be disillusioned in President Harrison who failed to back changes proposed by the Commissioner. After one conference at the White House, Theodore exploded, "Heavens, how I like positive men!" On the other hand, the President complained, "T. R. wants to put an end to all the evil in the world between sunrise and sunset." Even friends who approved of the Commissioner's reforms, disagreed with the aggressive methods he used to push them through. His statements to the press were sprinkled like red pepper through the newspapers, and the more he said, the less care he showed for facts. Finally, Cabot Lodge and Edith protested, and only then was he subdued into assuming a "statesmanlike reserve."

During those years with the Commission, 1889 to 1895, Washington was "just a big village." Theodore's financial troubles made it necessary for him to take a small house off Connecticut Avenue. (The ranching experiment had been so costly, there was now some doubt as to whether or not he could keep Sagamore.) The family was growing, which increased expenses. Kermit was born in 1889 and Ethel followed in 1891. If Edith had not been an expert manager, her husband might have gone bankrupt. But on the slimmest budget imaginable, Edith became one of Washington's most popular hostesses.

Since the Roosevelts could not afford the champagne parties other government notables gave, they made a celebration of their Sunday evening teas. Soon, those who dominated the political scene were competing for invitations to these teas that brought together the witty, charming, influential people of the Capitol. Theodore never lacked for stimulating conversation. He knew John Hay, Henry Adams, William Howard Taft, Thomas B. Reed (distinguished Speaker of the House of Representatives), and, of course, the Lodges. He entertained international celebrities, Rudyard Kipling and Richard Harding Davis, authors, and the artists, Augustus St. Gaudens and John Sargent. In addition to cultivating this lively social variety, a family closeness was being formed which would always characterize the Roosevelts.

Alice and Theodore, Kermit and Ethel would wait on the corner of Farragut Square for their father to come from the office. The moment he jumped off the streetcar, they surrounded him, tugging and kissing with equal vigor. From his pockets he would take small toys for them. Toy horses and cows were favorites, because they knew that when they reached home their father would heat a wire hairpin red hot, then they would brand the "cattle." Sometimes this led to an informal history lesson. Theodore would tell the children stories about Davey Crockett, Daniel Boone, the famous battles of the Civil War, and the Alamo. Tales of the Indian wars terrified Alice and Ethel, but they loved the sound of their father's voice and the way he acted out the high points of the stories. For all of the young Roosevelts, it was a "fun" way to learn American history.

Making history by reforming policies in the Civil Service was not always fun for Theodore; many of the established politicians resented the changes upon which the Commissioner insisted. "He acts as though he's the only man on the Commission — dictates to the rest of us!" was a common complaint. It took more than complaints to discourage Theodore once he made up his mind. He was sure that the only fair way for Civil Service appointments to be made was by competitive examination. And he was amazed at the number of congressmen who opposed such a procedure because some of their constituents, to whom they had promised political plums, would be unable to pass the exams. These politicians could not afford exposure, so they began a campaign of ridicule and set up numerous committees of investigation.

One leader in the Senate gave a speech about "a bright young man from Baltimore," who went before the Commission with letters of highest recommendation. The first question asked him was: "What is the shortest route from Baltimore to China?" The Senator claimed that the questioning then branched off into geology, chemistry, steamship lines from the U.S. to Europe, and that finally the "bright young man from Baltimore" was turned down because he did not know the answers to such ridiculous, unrelated questions.

In his usual fiery style, Roosevelt denied the charge. He proved that there were no questions in the examinations resembling those described by the Senator. He also demanded that "the bright young man" be identified. The Senator, nonplussed, led Roosevelt to the sarcastic conclusion: "This poor young man is without a name."

Not all of the Commissioner's reforms produced

ideal results. He was the first one to admit that. But under him the services of government offices increased in efficiency, and the merit system eliminated some of the corrupt power of unscrupulous political bosses.

From the experiences with the Civil Service Commission, Roosevelt learned one basic fact that was to disturb him throughout his years of serving the public: *good citizens* are often reluctant to participate in government beyond casting a vote. It is their indifference and hopelessness that make it possible for greedy men of self-interest to hold posts of political influence. To say that the latter were the only men who opposed Roosevelt would be untrue. But they did everything possible to limit his growing authority.

During the last months of President Harrison's term, Theodore felt uncertain about his future. He had said many unflattering things about the Democratic President-elect, Grover Cleveland, in a coast-to-coast campaign. To his surprise, Cleveland agreed with the reforms in which he believed and asked the young Commissioner to continue in office.

For two more years Roosevelt ran the bureau, but when asked if he would accept an appointment to be head of the New York Police Commission, he said yes. He knew he had done all he could do for Civil Service.

15

Undoubtedly, there were many politicians in Washington who were glad to see Roosevelt leave. And there were many in New York who hated to see him come. The new mayor of New York, William L. Strong, wanted to convince the public that his Republican administration could clean up the city, which had the reputation of being "a very hotbed of ... debauchery...."

The Police Department was as fat and lazy as its individual patrolmen. Blackmail, gambling, vice, graft, lawbreaking of every kind thrived. Protection money paid by lawbreakers was channeled through the police to political bosses. Law and crime both profited from this cooperation. Into the sordid situation charged Theodore Roosevelt. One of four commissioners appointed to administer the Police Department, he captured full attention for himself from the beginning. He seemed to take for granted that he was spokesman for the board, while the other officials went unnoticed. Their criticism was ignored, and both friend and enemy had to admit that Roosevelt backed up his words with action.

The newspapers reported all of the action. They also poked fun at the new Commissioner's costumes. On hot summer days he wore a pink shirt, tails out. For a heavy vest, he substituted a black silk sash. Although he was in excellent health, he was gaining weight and looked older than his thirty-seven years. The combination of outlandish dress and paunchy figure gave the cartoonists a heyday; he looked more like a Mexican bandit than a Police official.

They also portrayed him in police helmet, a billy club in hand, jumping from behind bushes to surprise patrolmen caught in the act of accepting bribes from notorious characters. In all of the cartoons, T.R.'s glasses protected squinting eyes, and his teeth were exaggerated into his most prominent feature, so that he was drawn as either fierce or childish. He laughed at the cartoons.

As he had done in the Civil Service Commission, Roosevelt soon put the police appointment and promotions on a merit basis. The ability of a man was matched to the department needs without regard to political loyalties. Such a radical change in practice was given wide publicity.

Every charge of corruption was openly probed. In the same way, outstanding acts of heroism were, for the first time, recognized, gallantry rewarded. Honesty became something more than a joke. And the Law gained respect instead of being ignored. The men on the Force came to like Roosevelt. He won their loyalty the way he had won the friendship of the cowboys on the ranch; he was fair; he worked harder than anyone else; without fear he enforced the law "up to the handle"; he learned first hand all he could about conditions in the districts where crime was a way of life.

A reporter, Jacob Riis, had written a book describing the stark realities of the slums. It was titled, *How the Other Half Lives,* and it so impressed Roosevelt that he called Riis to his office and asked him personally to show him the things about which he had written. The two men became great friends. At any hour of day or night, they could be seen in the tenement district as they inspected housing and talked with the poor.

It was the first time the well-to-do Theodore had come face to face with the evils and desperation of poverty, and he was shocked to realize that the New York City government pretended they did not exist. A still greater shock was in store when he discovered that men of wealth and influence in Wall Street contributed to the lot of the slum-dwellers since some of them owned the unsanitary, condemned tenements. Neither the police nor the Public Health departments took any responsibility for the disease and crime that flourished.

Theodore was convinced that government could prevent such inequalities, and the public should be made aware of them. "I was getting our social, industrial, and political need into . . . perspective," he wrote. He was concerned with the rights of everyone, not just the rights of a few. Though his background could have scarcely differed more from that of his boyhood hero, Abraham Lincoln, he was developing Lincoln's type of democratic conscience. A practical example is evident in his handling of labor disputes. He was determined that labor unions would have their rights. At the same time, he used the Police Department to control labor riots that threatened the order of New York City during his years as Commissioner.

When he left the office, union leaders urged him to stay. They praised his liberal attitude toward organized labor and called him "a champion of the working man with a desire to do the right thing no matter what the cost."

Not everyone was so complimentary. He was accused of appointing a woman to be secretary to the president of the Police Board in order to create a sensation. His enforcement of Sunday "blue laws" prohibiting the sale of liquor was called adolescent. His speaking engagements outside New York in behalf of the Republican Presidential candidate, William McKinley, brought up the charge that he was neglecting the duties for which he was being paid.

By 1897 Roosevelt had made so many political enemies, he told friends he did not expect to survive in public office. It was true that the Platt machine which controlled New York City officials at the time hated him more than ever. But his activities in the Police Commission had made him a national figure. His reputation for efficiency, honesty and courage was described even in foreign papers. And if he had not as yet learned diplomacy, the art of getting along with other politicians, he had been exposed to the major social problems of his time. That added significantly to his preparation for larger office.

When Jacob Riis and Lincoln Steffens suggested he would some day be a Presidential candidate, he practically shouted, "Don't you dare mention such a thing! . . . I won't let myself think about it. . . . If I do think about it, I'll become careful, calculating, cautious. . . ."

Besides, helping McKinley win the presidency was his number one concern right then, and he was the most vigorous of all campaigners. On March 5, 1897, Inauguration Day, Theodore was delighted to read the New York *Tribune* headline: "Republicans Take Helm. Under Bright Skies and with Fair Winds, the Ship of State Sails for the Haven of Prosperity."

16

McKinley had no choice. He must reward Roosevelt for contributing to the Republican victory. The question was, where could he place such an aggressive party man with the least chance of stirring up trouble? Roosevelt had pronounced views on every national issue. It wouldn't do for him to get into a position to try them out. Perhaps he would be harmless enough as Assistant Secretary of the Navy, a post which allowed a minimum of authority. Secretary Long, who would be Theodore's chief, was an ex-governor of Massachusetts, an elegant old gentleman with white hair and mustache, who, at sixty, was as conservative as Theodore was brash. Certainly Long would have a restraining influence.

Even a President can yield to wishful thinking. In no time at all, Roosevelt's enthusiasm carried him beyond the plans of Secretary Long and the approval of McKinley. He forgot his pledge to keep his ideas to himself and plunged into the national debate. One school of thought proposed peace with all other countries of the world, even though the Monroe Doctrine was being flouted by Spain. Roosevelt labeled the men of this school "futile sentimentalists" in favor of "peace at any price" who would bring about a "flabby, timid type of character."

He took the opposite view. Freedom must be defended at any cost, including war if necessary, and for this stand he was called belligerent and a Jingoist. Supported by Cabot Lodge, he won quite a following. President Elliott of Harvard was indignant that two graduates of that noble school would hold "this doctrine of Jingoism, this chip-on-the-shoulder attitude . . . of a ruffian and a bully." He declared Lodge and Roosevelt were "degenerated sons of Harvard."

These contrasting points of view continue to be subjects for debate. Maybe they always will be. And maybe Theodore would have been a peace-at-any-price man, had he not overcome the physical handicaps of illness and weakness in childhood. Stronger boys threatened and bullied him until, by sheer determination, he developed into a strong, robust man of action able to defend himself against any comer. For whatever reason, the Assistant Secretary of the Navy felt the only way for the United States to get along with hostile Germany and France, ambitious Japan, competitive England, was to be strong, able to answer any threat with might.

He had always taken a special interest in the navy. The first of his books published was *The History of the Naval War of 1812*, and from the moment he became Assistant Secretary, he had done what he could to prepare his country for action. He ordered battleships built, ammunition distributed, appointed a new commander of the Asiatic Fleet, Admiral George Dewey. Having learned that the marksmanship of the fighting crews aboard U.S. navy ships was laughable, he revamped all training programs. Older, incompetent officers were retired.

Some Washington officials claimed this feverish preparation would bring on war. Roosevelt preached that it was the surest way to keep peace. "I abhor injustice and bullying by the strong at the expense of the weak," he said. "I abhor violence and bloodshed. I believe war should never be resorted to when, or so long as, it is honorably possible to avoid it. I respect all men and women who, from high motives and with sanity and self-respect, do all they can to avert war. I advocate preparation for war in order to avert war, and I should never advocate war unless it was the only alternative to dishonor."

In January of 1896, newspapers carried sensational stories about cruelties being practiced by Spanish rulers on their subjects in Cuba. That island, next door to Florida, was in a state of chaos and anarchy. Trade with the United States was almost at a standstill. Our large tobacco and sugar interests were being depleted. On every hand the question was raised, should we rescue Cuba from the oppression of Spain? Roosevelt declared, "It is our duty . . . to stop the devastation and destruction." Some agreed. Some said no, we have no rights in Cuba.

This issue may not have led to war had it not been for two incidents. The Spanish ambassador carelessly left a letter on his desk which referred to President McKinley as a weakling politician who wanted to please everyone, including the war-makers. The truth was, McKinley was doing all he could to keep peace, in spite of the war-makers. The revelation of the letter would not have changed his policy even though it was insulting. But the American press blew the personal insult into a national one, making it seem that the honor of the United States had been attacked.

The following month, in Havana Harbor, the U.S.S. *Maine* exploded and sank. Two officers and 264 men were killed. The ship had been sent to Havana by the President as "an act of friendly courtesy," and Spain had received it with diplomatic hospitality. Overnight, friendliness changed to hostility.

The Jingoists said the Spaniards were responsible; such treachery must be revenged. Fighting fever swept the United States. McKinley's last ditch efforts to prevent war provoked Roosevelt to remark that the President had no more backbone than a chocolate éclair. Rumors spread that the Spanish fleet was on its way to bombard American shores. The Assistant Secretary of the Navy asked the President to give notice to Spain that if the fleet sailed, it would be regarded as an act of war.

Tension mounted. A court of inquiry found on March 20, 1898, that the *Maine* had been sunk by a submarine mine. This finding was reported to the Congress on the 28th. From coast to coast the cry was taken up, "Remember the *Maine!*"

McKinley was not powerful enough to control the situation and on April 21 he declared war on Spain.

Suddenly, regardless of what brought it on, war was a fact. To everyone's surprise, Theodore Roosevelt resigned his position of Assistant to the Secretary of the Navy. He could not bear the thought of sitting behind a desk in the Capitol when he could be at "the front." As usual, he wanted to get into the action. He asked Alger, Secretary of the War Department, a man with whom he had influence, to get him into a newly formed Volunteer Cavalry. Alger offered Theodore command of a regiment, but brief military training in the National Guard was scarcely a qualification for such responsibility, so Theodore suggested his old friend, Army Surgeon Leonard Wood. Alger finally made Wood a colonel and Roosevelt a lieutenant-colonel.

When their regiment assembled at San Antonio, it resembled the cast for a wild-west show more than anything military. Most of the men were from the plains of Arizona, New Mexico, Oklahoma, Texas — Southwesterners. "Dead Shot" Joe may have been typical; according to "reports," he could put a bullet through a jack rabbit's eye at one thousand yards while riding a wild bronco. Some of these cowboys were too independent to salute officers. Admirers of Roosevelt from eastern colleges also joined the group, but the rest of the army and the public thought of it as rough-and-ready. The nickname, Rough Riders, stuck, and a sign at the San Antonio railroad station read, "This Way to the Roosevelt Rough Rider Camp." Colonel Wood may have been the commander, but his lieutenant-colonel was in charge.

The preceding fall, the Roosevelt's fifth child, Quentin, had been born. Afterward, Edith was seriously ill. It was only natural that she and Cabot Lodge tried to talk Theodore out of going to Cuba. His colleagues in government pleaded with him. He would not listen. In 1898, war was still considered romantic, even glamorous, and although Theodore's decision to participate was judged recklessly adolescent by many, it was also sincere. He was back with his favorite kind of men. And he was on horseback again. There was danger ahead.

Some historians have accused him of fraternizing with his troops in a way that weakened Colonel Wood's discipline over the regiment. Others have said he bolstered the morale of the regiment by talking man-to-man with anyone who came to him. "He's human," one Rough Rider said. "That's why we follow him." That he was adored by the First Volunteer Cavalry cannot be questioned.

On May 29 the Rough Riders left for Tampa, their port of embarkation. Upon arriving four days later, they found a scene of "wildest confusion." General Miles, who was supposed to be supervising the loading of troops and supplies, was in no way experienced for the job, and disorder took over.

Roosevelt's frustration must have been colossal. He

had tried while still in the Navy Department to get the War Department to organize for such a moment. He remembered the day he had been called to the office of one of the highest ranking military men. Everyone knew that war was about to be declared. In Roosevelt's opinion, the officer should have been "working eighteen hours out of twenty-four on the vital problems ahead of him." Instead, he wanted suggestions on the placement of pockets on the jackets of new uniforms for enlisted men.

When Theodore asked another officer how he planned to equip his men, he answered he would give each soldier two revolvers and a lariat, then turn them loose. At the last minute, Roosevelt had been able to get lightweight uniforms issued to the Rough Riders. The War Department had ordered woolen clothing for the campaign in the tropics!

He was not surprised, then, to find that no arrangements had been made in Tampa for a ship to transport his regiment to Daiquiri. In effect, he and Woods commandeered the transport *Yucatan,* and jammed their men onto it. There was almost no room to walk around the deck and the trip took nine days. Upon docking, the Rough Riders disembarked "higgledy-piggledy"; who got ashore first did not matter, and how one got ashore was a matter of initiative. Certainly Theodore did not wait to take his turn.

Cuban scouts reported that the Spanish forces had fled to Santiago. By June 23, the cavalry was on its way in pursuit. Not on charging horses as they had visualized, but on foot; they might as well have been the humble infantry. The cowboys were not accustomed to walking on jungle trails, and the pace set by Colonel Wood resulted in fifty men falling out from exhaustion. When they halted to rest, the enemy fired on them. Sixteen men were killed in this first skirmish, many were wounded.

The military objective was to drive the Spanish out of Cuba, but the army and navy were not in agreement as to how to do it. Neither branch seemed eager to get involved, one expecting the other to engage the Spaniards first. The army commander, Major General W. R. Shafter, was ill from the heat. Only a man like himself, who weighed 300 pounds and suffered from gout, could understand how demoralizing heat could be.

The commissary department collapsed, leaving the troops without food for days. The only things in good supply were Theodore's glasses; he had brought along twelve pairs. Conditions were terrible enough to dishearten the toughest veteran. Not T.R. He organized foraging parties and gave them money from his own pocket to buy supplies from friendly Cubans. He visited the field hospitals, tirelessly cheering the wounded. And when, on June 30, orders came at last for the advance on Santiago, he was ready.

His regiment led the second brigade down the jungle trail behind the first brigade. They were to cross a stream at the foot of a hill, then turn right and follow a stream until they joined with the infantry. From an opposite hill, they were being watched by the Spanish, who began firing as soon as the Americans reached the stream. The first brigade halted and spread out, finding cover as best it could, and began returning the fire. Then the second brigade followed suit. Roosevelt sent word to the command at the rear that he wanted permission to lead the men in an attack on the hills in front of him. The enemy was firing on the exposed troops with fatal accuracy. "Bullets drove in sheets" on all sides. Finally an order came to advance. Roosevelt was to support the

regular cavalry with the specific objective of taking a red-tiled ranch house on one of the hills. (This hill was later named Kettle Hill by the Rough Riders.)

For some reason the order did not reach the first brigade, and since there was no one with rank superior to Theodore's, he offered to include them in his order to advance. When they made no move to follow him, he commanded, "Then let my men through." As he led the second brigade through the lines, the regulars of the first began joining him one by one until it was necessary for him to mount horseback in order to keep in touch with all of his men.

Now, he waved his wide-brimmed hat, spurred his horse and charged up the enemy's hill, followed by the regulars *and* volunteers, many of whom were already wounded. And it was a miracle that any of them survived that assault of Kettle Hill, because the fighting was close as they stormed the Spanish entrenchments.

In retrospect, Roosevelt said, "If there had been any one in high command to supervise and press the attack that afternoon, we would have gone right into Santiago." Instead, he received orders to halt his men, stay on the crest of the hill they had taken, and hold it.

That night, captured provisions provided the hungry, exhausted troops with the first decent meal they had had in a week. And the Spaniards did not open fire again until sunrise the next morning. Men were wounded and killed in the same trench with Theodore; shells landed so close to him, they blackened him with powder, but he was unharmed. For two days the Americans were pinned down and, without reinforcements, it looked as though the whole maneuver would turn into a major military disaster. On Sunday, July 3, General Shafter wired Washington that he would be forced to retreat unless the

U.S. naval forces fought their way into Santiago Harbor. That same day, the Admiral leading the Spanish fleet, foolishly ventured out from the harbor and was defeated by the U.S. Navy. Santiago then fell to the Americans without further action from the Rough Riders. Wood was promoted to the rank of brigadier general and put in command of captured Santiago. Colonel Roosevelt succeeded him in the command of the volunteer brigade, and in less than four weeks the Spanish had been driven from Cuba.

Whatever the threat to American shores, real or imagined, it was over. The warriors could return home as heroes. But no order came from Washington for them to return. Yellow fever and malaria broke out among the poorly fed troops. If they were not moved out of the tropical climate soon, more would be lost to fever than had died in battle. Roosevelt drafted a letter of protest, setting forth the conditions of the men and the prospect of their being wiped out by disease. A similar round robin letter was signed by a number of generals. By design, both of these letters came into the possession of an Associated Press correspondent who published them. The War Department was forced to act at last; the Santiago regiments sailed for home, to arrive on August 15. One month later, the Rough Riders were mustered out and said good-bye to their colonel.

"Don't go back and lie on your laurels," Roosevelt told them. "They'll wither."

17

No one needed to give Roosevelt such advice. He expected to rest at Sagamore from his military adventure, but a stream of visitors, including Rough Riders, newsmen, politicians, relatives, kept him as busy as ever. Now, he was America's number one patriot. As much as Republican boss Platt disliked Theodore, he wanted a winning candidate for governor of New York, and his gambler's instinct told him that the people were in a mood to elect a hero of the Spanish War. Roosevelt was nominated. By Election Day, the Democratic candidate was all but branded a traitor as he had not fought in Cuba for his country, and a vote for the Republican candidate amounted to a vote for the Stars and Stripes. The week before, Roosevelt had made 102 speeches. When he went to Oyster Bay to cast his own vote on Election Day, he was tense and worn out.

Two reporters arriving at Sagamore that evening, found Theodore in the library reading. Alice and Edith were nearby. As the evening wore on without any word from the state chairman about the outcome of the election, one of the reporters tired of waiting, volunteered to go to the nearest telegraph office for the final message. A little after midnight word came of Roosevelt's victory, and the reporter rushed back to Sagamore with the announcement. The Governor-elect had gone to bed. The reporter rang the doorbell until Roosevelt opened the door in his nightshirt.

"You've won!" shouted the reporter carried away

with the triumph. "That's bully!" said the Governor-elect sleepily.

By the end of December, 1898, the Roosevelts were saying sad farewells to their beloved Sagamore and moving into the huge, ugly house in Albany, misleadingly called the Executive Mansion.

On Inauguration Day, the children gasped at the sight of troops and officials in splendid uniforms; the ceremony was solemn. They were proud of their father who was the center of all the attention. Edith was proud, too, but she could not look at Theodore as he took the oath of office for fear her tears of joy would embarrass him.

According to custom she would have to stand in the receiving line at the inaugural reception to follow, and shake hands with each guest. No one could shake that many hands without fainting from exhaustion, she decided, so as the six thousand guests of the Governor crowded past that day, she did not shake hands, but simply smiled. Her smile was so warm and genuine no one noticed that an old foolish custom had been ignored.

In his first message to the legislature, Governor Theodore Roosevelt called for tax reforms, improved civil service laws, concern for organized labor, overhaul of the Tammany Hall machine in New York City, and economy. By the end of his first year in office, progress had been made in most of these areas.

This was probably due to one reality every politician must accept. He cannot get his programs adopted without the cooperation of whoever controls the legislature. Senator Platt was the man in this case, and the new Governor learned to trade with him. In exchange for appointing Platt's men to public jobs (if they were competent), Platt backed the Governor's reforms, even though he disagreed with them in many cases. The independents, who had considered Roosevelt their leader, misunderstood this seeming collaboration, but from it progressive legislation developed.

It was the first time a New York governor had the courage to suggest laws to tax the tremendous profits corporations were collecting from public franchises. For instance, a privately owned company obtained from the government a license and franchise to operate a public transportation system. The company claimed that since this was a service to the public, the fares received were not taxable profits.

Roosevelt sent a message to the Assembly demanding a reform bill which would make these profits taxable. Platt was furious. The Speaker of the Assembly, under Platt's control, tore up the message without even reading it to the Assembly.

When the Governor heard what had happened, he said, "I have a copy of my message. Take it to the Speaker and tell him if he doesn't read it to the Assembly, I will take the floor and deliver the speech myself!"

Platt could not risk that; the Speaker read the Governor's message. The Assembly passed the franchise tax bills.

It was the first time anyone had successfully stood up to Platt, and he did not like being beaten. Something would have to be done about Roosevelt, whom he called "a perfect bull in a china shop." Every trick in the political game was familiar to the canny Republican party boss, and he began scheming a way to keep Roosevelt in the limelight, while at the same time, taking away his rapidly spreading power. Could there be a better place for him than in the Vice-Presidency? Not only was Platt plotting to curtail his rival's power, he was forcing him to commit political suicide.

And so word went out to the party workers: Start a boom for T. R. — McKinley's running mate in 1900.

As Platt was sure it would, the scheme worked.

Even though Roosevelt wanted to continue for another term as governor of New York, he yielded to the wishes of the national convention — a convention that had seemingly been tricked into cutting short the future of its most promising leader.

It was obvious to visitors in the convention gallery that day that one observer was displeased with the decision. Edith Roosevelt, who seldom expressed political opinions, did not want her husband to accept the nomination for the secondary post, which in those days was insignificant. She knew the Vice President did nothing but campaign for the President and preside over the Senate; he was Mr. Nobody. She also knew that in no time Theodore would be bored with the role. He was interested in such a variety of subjects that some writers had compared him with the exuberant Benjamin Franklin, and like Franklin, he held strong opinions on every subject. Theodore would never be content to let others make all of the decisions and the speeches. As soon as the administration failed to act when he thought it should, or did something of which he disapproved, he would be bound to make an indiscreet comment to a reporter, get involved in a public controversy and spoil his chances ever to become President.

No, Edith was not pleased with the nomination. She was convinced her husband was destined for the Presidency, and this was the surest way for him to be sidetracked from that goal.

The national chairman of the Republican party,

Mark Hanna, was not pleased with the nomination either, but as soon as it became a hard, political fact, he informed Roosevelt that the burden of the Presidential campaign would fall on him; he would be expected to win the votes of the doubtful states. The candidate assured Mr. Hanna that he was "as strong as a bull moose" and would do all he could for the Grand Old Party.

On one tour alone, Roosevelt made 673 speeches in 567 towns. Before the campaign ended, he traveled 21,209 miles. At least 3,000,000 people heard him speak.

No matter how busy he was, he managed to have time with the family at Sagamore. He would not permit even a campaign to interfere with their traditional celebration of the Fourth of July, which began before dawn with the explosion of giant firecrackers. Breakfast was at 8:30, a noisy, cheerful gathering. Then there were games and "scrambly" walks, races on foot, on horses, in boats. Quentin had his piggy-back rides; Archie, his swimming lesson; Alice, a set of tennis; Kermit and Ted, several shooting contests. They climbed the trees in the apple orchard, romped in the barnloft, took turns in the pony cart. Sagamore Hill swarmed with cousins who joined all of the fun, and that meant everyone took a slide down Cooper's Bluff, a sandy hill about 200 feet high, with a sharp slope toward the beach. Theodore took the lead, followed by children of all ages and shapes, somersaulting, sliding, rolling after — shooting straight into the water. The resulting bruises and cuts were considered badges of daring.

In the afternoon everyone piled into a gaily decorated wagon and drove over to Oyster Bay where an Independence Day affair had been planned hastily. "Looks like the whole county is turning out," exclaimed little Ted as he watched people come from all directions —

farmers, driving their two-seated buckboards; wealthy "summer people' in expensive broughams. Most of the stores in town were closed. Flags were flying from the houses that lined the streets. In Audrey Park across from the railroad station, a crowd of over 2,000 gathered around a stand draped in red, white and blue bunting. As the Roosevelts drove up, a band blasted "Hail, Columbia!" and firecrackers drowned out the Baptist pastor's invocation.

Theodore had to push his way to the stand. Neighbors stopped him to shake hands and slap him on the back. He was their neighbor as well as the governor of New York. And according to the Episcopal rector's introduction, he would soon be the President of the United States. The local Roman Catholic priest shouted "Amen!" to that prophecy. His friends, too, believed he could not be stopped by the vice-presidency, and they all began cheering as Theodore took his place on the stand, looking as pleased as a small boy with all the fuss.

He made a short speech on his favorite subject of true Americanism, as the old men shouted, "You tell 'em, Teddy!" and the ladies in their starched shirtwaists tittered behind palm leaf fans at his jokes. The children clapped their hands when the grownups laughed; everyone was having a good time. They felt at home with Theodore. And he felt at home with the folk of Oyster Bay. If it were left up to them, they would have made him President right then and there. That's what many of them said to him afterward.

His sons and daughters helped set off the fireworks that evening. Roman candles, pinwheels, rockets, sparklers, bombs swished and banged, as the children jumped up and down and squealed. It was what Theodore called a "dee-lightful" day. He would recall it with pleasure in the days ahead when he was far from home, weary with campaigning.

The rest of the summer was devoted to speech-making, and by October, even the "bull moose" was worn out. His voice had failed him, and his ideas had gone stale. He was frankly annoyed by criticism flying at him from all sides. Some said he was neglecting his duties in the governor's office. His literary efforts were ridiculed. He had accused Quakers of being unworthy citizens because they refused to fight, and he was forced to apologize. The tension mounted to the breaking point, but just in time the November election brought victory. Because of his all-out effort, the McKinley-Roosevelt ticket received a plurality of 849,000 votes. Whether he liked it or not, Theodore was going to be Vice President of the United States.

18

Alice was up early on the morning of March 4, 1901. It was Inauguration Day. Washington teemed with visitors. Fortunately, Alice and Ethel and the boys and their mother could stay at Auntie Bye's house on "N" Street. And all of them were up early "eager to see the show start."

A squadron of smartly uniformed soldiers took the Vice President-elect to the Capitol, and the family followed in a carriage provided for them. The crowded Senate chamber hummed with anticipation as Theodore Roosevelt was escorted to the speaker's rostrum.

Ted and Kermit and Archie hung over the railing of the gallery, their jackets sprouting campaign buttons of all sizes. Alice, sophisticated at seventeen, dressed smartly for the occasion, sat quietly beside Edith.

I do wish the boys would act more grown up, she thought. And Ethel — she isn't much better with those vulgar McKinley-Roosevelt buttons decorating her chest!

But the moment her father began speaking she forgot her brothers and sisters existed. How handsome Father looks in his frock coat and striped trousers. He even has a red carnation in his button-hole. He's so dignified and poised. I love his voice.

"Mother, he's speaking very softly, but you can hear every word," Alice whispered to Edith, who listened thoughtfully to her husband as he warmed to his speech.

The oratory of President McKinley did not altogether hold Alice's attention. I hope it has stopped drizzling, she thought. Why does it have to rain today of all days? My velvet collar will get spotted — the parade will be spoiled too — I wish I didn't have to go to that dull luncheon at the White House — the McKinleys seem so mousy! I wish it were evening so that I could dress for the ball — Father will adore my white point d'esprit gown. . . .

So the day of ceremony passed for Alice, who never stopped comparing her father with the President and resenting the waste of her father's talents in an office of only minor significance.

Finally, it was time to gather in the Blue Room just before the Inaugural Ball. Alice looked around the room musing. I've lived through this tiresome day just for the ball — surely *it* will be gay and elegant. Mother and Father look so young and stylish beside the McKinleys. Oh, here come the Hays — Secretary of State Hay, I should say — and his wife and Alice and Helen. They're the prettiest! I do wish I were as old as they.

The Hay girls walked straight across the room to Alice, stretching out white-gloved hands toward her, their smiles gracious and easy.

"Alice, what a charming gown," cooed Helen. "New, isn't it, dear?"

"Yes," said Alice. "One's father isn't inaugurated every day, you know."

"Well, I wish *our* father would get elected to something so that *we* could have an excuse for something new — these old taffetas!"

Alice suddenly realized how accustomed the Hay sisters were to state functions. The ball was no novelty to them. My new gown might as well be a bright red curtain, she thought, everyone knows it's just for tonight. All of these people are watching me and thinking, *this* person is very *young*. How humiliating!

But the tall and lovely Alice soon forgot the imagined inappropriateness of her gown in the brilliant company assembled for the Inaugural Ball. There were at least a thousand guests. She had never attended anything so grand as this. From the President's box in the gallery she could watch everyone below. Perched on the arm of a chair near the gallery railing, she listed mentally the important personages she recognized.

"Alice, can't you find a better place to sit?" asked Helen Hay in a loud whisper. "You're obscuring Mrs. McKinley's view."

For the first time Alice looked to see who was sitting in the chair. It was that frail little inconspicuous Mrs. McKinley, the President's wife! Alice jumped up, blushing. I do hope Father gets to be President, she thought, so that I can have lots of practice being a lady!

19

Spring and summer passed uneventfully. The Senate adjourned soon after the inauguration, and Theodore Roosevelt, Vice President, dreaded the inactivity ahead of him. He enjoyed being with the family at Sagamore, but he must think of new ways to fill his time. He invited undergraduates from Yale and Harvard to visit him so that he could discuss with them his goals of decent and honest government. They, with their sense of high purpose, were the future hope of the country; he must influence them to enter public life. In addition to these forums, Theodore arranged with Chief Justice White to complete legal courses he had abandoned years before. He attended the opening of the Pan-American Exposition at Buffalo, N. Y., where he made a speech. He made many speeches that summer, but always he remembered to subordinate his ideas to those of the President. It was not easy to do.

Ted had been away at school for the first time, so Theodore planned a four day vacation cruise for Ted and Kermit and their cousins. It was a huge success, because no one had to wash. There were the other Sagamore pastimes — riding and swimming, tennis and baseball. Alice, alone, did not participate. She was too "mature" for sweaty games. She was proving her independence.

In September, Edith took the children to the Tahawas Club in the Adirondacks for the mountain air. The plan was for Theodore to join them there after attending an outing on Lake Champlain where he was to be the honored guest of the Vermont Fish and Game League. On September 6, as he stood in a reception line

shaking hands with admirers, he was interrupted by a phone call from Buffalo. He could not believe what the distant voice said to him: "The President has been shot! Take the next train to Buffalo."

The news shocked Roosevelt deeply. He forgot his own ambition in his affectionate concern for McKinley, whom he had come to respect as a friend. Upon arriving in Buffalo the following day, he was assured that the President was not injured as seriously as had been feared. The attempted assassination had been frustrated. By September 10, the reports were so optimistic, Roosevelt took the train back to his family in the Adirondacks.

With Edith, Ethel and Kermit, two guides and several friends, he hiked five miles up the trail to Mount Marcy. On the shores of Colden Lake the party spent the night in two cabins. The next morning, after breakfast, the Vice President and the other men decided to climb on to the top of the mountain. They reached the summit at twenty minutes past twelve. After enjoying the spectacular view, the party started down the mountain and found an ideal place beside a lake to stop for lunch. As they perched on rocks and stumps eating sandwiches, a familiar figure ran up the trail toward them. It was the woodsman, Harrison Hall, with a slip of paper in his hand which he gave to Roosevelt without a word.

The message was from Elihu Root, Secretary of War, and Theodore knew before he read it that the news was bad. "The President appears to be dying," the telegram said. "Lose no time in coming."

Racing at breakneck speed, three relays of horses and three relays of daring drivers took Roosevelt through murky darkness, over thirty-five miles of steep, rain-rutted roads to a special train waiting at North Creek. His secretary met him as he jumped from the buckboard and ran to the railroad car. "The President is dead," the secretary said simply. "Everyone is waiting for you."

PART THREE
1901 - 1909

20

Theodore Roosevelt became President of the United States six weeks before his forty-third birthday — the youngest man ever to hold his country's highest office.

Three other Vice Presidents had succeeded to the Presidency as he did, and in each case policy had been abruptly reversed—plunging the government into chaos. In order to avoid confusion at a time when the nation was numb with disaster, Theodore pledged to continue the programs of McKinley. "If any man is fit to be President, he will speedily impress himself in the office so that the policies pursued will be his anyhow, and he will not have to bother as to whether he is changing them or not . . . the important thing is that his subordinates shall make a success of handling their several departments." All members of the assassinated President's cabinet were asked to stay on, though they were older and more conservative than Roosevelt.

The political bosses who had plotted his derailment only a short time before, quickly volunteered their cooperation. Secretary of State, John Hay (an elder statesman who had been private secretary to Lincoln and minister to Great Britain), had recently made disapproving remarks about Roosevelt. Now, Hay quickly sent his congratulations. Even the powerful men of Wall Street sent emissaries to make a truce with the new President.

To all of them he gave assurance. "I shall move slowly," he promised. This young man, described as "adolescent" by his enemies, and called "my sixth child" by his own wife, seemed suddenly matured by the burden and authority of his office.

At the peak of physical strength, imaginative and fearless, he could not have been more unlike his predecessor. He was eager to lead, to do anything "the Nation demands unless such action is forbidden by the Constitution. . ." The influence of the Chief Executive was about to be broadened in the cause of public welfare, the common interest of *all* the people.

First of all, he made political appointments on the basis of ability and honesty just as he had done in former positions. He was himself efficient and fair. He expected others to be. And he expected them to work. He tackled the top job in the country with energy and zest, doing the work of three or four men. An observer said the President was the busiest man he ever knew, but he seemed unhurried; his desk was always clear; he kept deadlines and appointments punctually; he gave no hint of worry or confusion in time of crisis. In other words, Roosevelt was a born executive, in a position at last to accomplish the goals in which he believed with his whole heart.

It was an era of change that complemented his progressive ideas. Since the Civil War, Washington, itself had been in transition. Broad avenues were replacing narrow streets — landscaped squares appeared where dilapidated shacks had been. A short time before, a single telephone had served the needs of the White House. A lone secretary handled the President's correspondence in longhand. Suddenly, a battery of stenographers and secretaries moved into the executive offices to serve him, and telephones were added one after another to care for the calls that came in day and night.

One thing remained the same: the White House was

as ugly and uncomfortable as ever. The floor plan was inconvenient—the decor depressing. Heavy, plush, gilded furniture, combined with a "forest" of potted palms, gave the mansion a smothering atmosphere which Alice once called "late General Grant and early Pullman."

There were advantages for the children, though. There was plenty of room for romps and games of hide-and-go-seek, and they could try their stilts and bicycles in the long upstairs hall. They ranged in age from Quentin, four, to eighteen-year-old Alice, who was planning a coming out party. The White House was so large it was almost impossible to keep track of the smaller children.

Edith became aware of this when a servant reported to her, in a voice choked with shock, "You know the staircase that leads to the private rooms at the west end of the hall, Ma'am?" Of course Edith knew the stairway. "Well, Ma'am, you won't believe your eyes what's going on there!" Edith put aside the letters she was writing and hurried to the stairway just in time to see Archie give Quentin a push. The two boys had managed to sneak some large tin trays from the pantry and were sliding down the banister in reckless style. Down sailed Quentin shrieking like a Comanche and landed with a clatter at his mother's feet. The look she gave the boys made words unnecessary.

Soon after taking office, Theodore had the old mansion remodeled more in keeping with his own tastes. The offices were modernized and space was added for entertaining. Space was needed for the family quarters, too, but Edith, in her capable fashion, managed to find room for the children, a governess, maid, housekeeper and family friends. It was just as well that young Ted was in school at Groton and that Alice preferred New York Society to that of Washington. To her, Washington meant endless publicity. Her picture was in every newspaper, abroad as well as in America. No wonder, of course. Alice was poised, haughty, beautiful and fashionable. Her regal grace and pompadour were imitated by all young ladies studying such things. The press reported her every move, and gave her the lofty title: "Princess Alice."

Ethel attracted less attention, and although she thought of herself as a young lady, too, she was still little-girl enough to filch nuts and candies from splendidly set tables in the state dining room.

Perhaps the boys suffered most from the difference between Washington and Sagamore Hill. Even though their father still had breakfast with them every morning and read to them every night before they went to bed, and even though he permitted them to bring pets and pals directly to his office, they could not be with him enough — not the way they had been at Sagamore. This meant they were also freer to get into mischief, and the whole nation followed their escapades in the daily papers.

One of the most familiar stories concerned Archie and Quentin. It seemed that Archie would never recover from a bad case of measles unless Quentin came up with a way to cheer him.

"I have a plan, Charlie," the younger boy said to a White House coachman, "but you'll have to help me with it."

"What's that, Master Quentin?"

"Let's take Algonquin up to see Archie." Algonquin was a pony. Being separated from him was undoubtedly prolonging Archie's illness.

"Which way we gonna bring Algonquin in the house, Master Quentin?"

"Right through the basement. You guide him, Charlie, while I think of a reason to send the guards up to the foyer on the first floor." Quentin would take care of the guards, but he was stumped about what to do with Algonquin once he was inside the White House. "How are we going to get him up all those stairs?" he asked Charlie.

"Stairs, Master Quentin? What's wrong with the elevator?" Charlie and Quentin took the pony by elevator to the upper floor of the White House for a gleeful reunion with Archie, who, sure enough, began getting better right away.

The children did not make all of the news. Their father was receiving more coverage by reporters than any other President had ever received. It may have been that he was doing more; there was more to report. But he must have tired of having stories written about every conference, including the most informal ones at breakfast, luncheon and dinner. Besides the press, the secret service was always at his elbow, a noticeable irritation.

In his first message to Congress, Theodore showed unusual restraint. He recognized that he must have both Republicans and Democrats behind him, but he did not hesitate to restate his position on issues unpopular with both parties, such as: needed control over large corporations; protection of organized labor; land and resource conservation; support of the Monroe Doctrine; a larger and better trained navy.

There were many side issues too, such as his policy of making political appointments based on merit. He was especially alarmed over the "scalawags" being sent as delegates to the national convention from the South. The Republican Party needed its reputation south of the Mason and Dixon line cleaned up. As a move in that direction, Roosevelt consulted with the great Negro educator, Dr. Booker T. Washington, about men of his race who deserved appointment on the basis of ability. Thomas Goode Jones of Alabama was consequently recommended by Dr. Washington, and the President selected him to be a U. S. district judge.

Theodore's background, which demonstrated tolerance for North and South alike, did not prepare him for the result. Whether the appointment of Judge Jones, or the role of Dr. Washington sparked the Southern revolt, who can be sure? But one thing *was* sure, Southerners considered it "monstrous" for the President to entertain a Negro at dinner in the White House, which Theodore had done in the course of his discussions with Booker T. Washington.

The New Orleans *Times-Democrat* fumed: "When Mr. Roosevelt sits down to dinner with a Negro, he declares that the Negro is the social equal of the white man." The New Orleans *Daily State* called the event "a studied insult." "The most damnable outrage ever . . . " cried the Memphis *Scimitar.*

Surprised and furious, Theodore replied, "I shall have Dr. Washington to dine as often as I please." But the damage had been done. His first political blunder as President was enormous and thwarted the reconciliation between the G. O. P. and the South, which had been his dream.

It did not discourage him from battle with another group just as surely to be insulted by his views as the southerners had been. These were industrialists, corporation magnates, railroad kings, such as Morgan, Gould Harriman and Hill. "Big money" interests were closely tied to the very life of the Republican party. Now, a Republican president was declaring, "I am neither for capital nor labor . . . I am for honesty against dishonesty, for patriotism against selfishness, for right against wrong." This President would see to it that every citizen, black or white, laborer or tycoon, got a "Square Deal."

The Northern Securities Company was the first combination of companies Roosevelt tackled. It, along with the United Steel Corporation, had been formed by J. P. Morgan. The newspapers described it as a $400,000,000 fund for the purchase of certain railroad securities with the real purpose of monopolizing these railroads in the rapidly developing northwest. Mr. Morgan said these charges were nonsense; his company would reorganize the nation's transportation in an orderly fashion. Everyone would benefit.

The President had come to fear "the tyranny of wealth." He was suspicious of the Northern Securities Company. If this was another monopoly being formed to raise rail rates, while at the same time lowering wages, its profits would soar, and its stocks could be manipulated to give the "mighty industrial overlords" more power than the government had.

Without consulting anyone other than his Attorney General, Roosevelt had the Federal government file a suit against the Northern Securities Company for breaking the law as set forth in the Sherman Anti-Trust Act. Wall Street was shocked. The business community had always winked at the Sherman Act. Why had the President decided to use it without warning? Did this mean he was going to interfere with other big business operations? The courts had never fought corporations before. There was no reason to think they would in this case.

Roosevelt assured the country that he had no desire to wipe out wealth nor the wealthy. But in the interest of all the people, he wanted the government to have a measure of control over large corporations. Needless to say, this did not win him the backing and confidence of Wall Street, and many of his old friends from childhood rebuked him.

It was not until 1904 that the Supreme Court ordered the Northern Securities Company dissolved for having violated the Sherman Act. Roosevelt's purpose in filing the suit had been served. The government had proved that it had the power to deal with big corporations if they disregarded the public's good.

21

For some time conditions had been scandalous in the coal-producing areas of Pennsylvania, Ohio and Illinois. In the year Roosevelt became President, the average wage of the worker in the mines was about $560 a year for ten and twelve hours work a day. Employment was irregular. There were no safety measures. Accidents were common. In that one year, 441 men had been killed.

By early spring of 1902, the smouldering problems of the miners broke into the open. Pennsylvania miners went on strike for an increase in pay, a shorter working day, and a fair weight. (They were usually paid for a 2,340 pound ton, when it more often weighed 2,700 to 4,000 pounds.)

The squalid living conditions of these workmen were indescribable. They were forced to live in company-owned huts and buy supplies from company stores at cut-throat prices.

Both sides, operators and miners, refused to talk. By May, 140,000 men were idle. By June, an appeal was sent to the President asking him to intervene. The truth was, there was no legal basis on which he could. The crisis worsened. Schools in New York City closed. Hoarded coal cost $35 a ton and winter was coming. The entire nation would suffer if there was not a settlement.

Concerned and frustrated, Roosevelt asked men from both sides of the dispute to the White House for a conference. He appointed an arbitration commission. The miners accepted the commission; the mine operators refused it. Another conference was called, with the same discouraging result. Theodore said of management, *"They* are not in danger of dying cold. It is the poor, the miners who will suffer."

As days passed without the operators agreeing to any of the commission's proposals, the public began to protest. As its anger grew, so did its support of Roosevelt grow. The next time the mine owners told him the strike was none of his business, he replied, "My business is the people's welfare." Public opinion finally pressured the owners into a settlement, and once again the people knew that the President was protecting their interests.

No one faction was going to enjoy special privileges at the expense of another. Class distinctions destroyed liberty. All Americans would be treated justly without regard for "class." The weak would no longer be exploited by the powerful few. As long as Theodore Roosevelt was President, the "Square Deal" was more than a slogan.

22

A few months before his death, McKinley appointed the Isthmian Canal Commission to decide the merits of two routes for a canal the United States wanted to build between the Atlantic and Pacific oceans. One route passed through Nicaragua, the other through Panama. France had already tried to build the canal and failed. But she owned rights in Panama and offered to sell them to the U.S. When Roosevelt heard that these rights could be had at a bargain, he naturally favored the Panama route. In time, after a revolution in Colombia, and much wrangling in Congress, the Panama route was agreed upon, and the gigantic engineering feat was begun. Great dams and locks were constructed to allow the largest ocean going ships to pass through, eliminating the long, 13,400 mile trip around Cape Horn.

Getting the canal started was one of Theodore's greatest accomplishments, in his own opinion. Certainly it was a step that strengthened the enforcement of the Monroe Doctrine which was the basis of his foreign policy. It also made possible the domination of the Caribbean by the U. S. navy.

By the spring of 1903, the President was looking forward to the election of the following year. He would have a chance to win office on his own record. Being President, he could not campaign since actively seeking re-election to the highest office was contrary to the custom of the time; that would be considered bad taste; therefore he must make the most of his opportunities in

1903. And so he toured cross-country from April till June that year. He should have been encouraged by the way he was received by the people, but his mood was gloomy. At an especially enthusiastic rally in Des Moines, Iowa, he made a vigorous speech and seemed exhilarated by the crowd. As soon as the train pulled away from the station, though, he spoke of the election with doubt. The cheers meant nothing, he said. The crowd would have been as loud for any other President; they were not for him, they were for the office. "They come to see the President much as they would come to see a circus . . . I will not kiss their babies!" For him it was the lonely moment that comes to all prominent elected officials. Roosevelt was sure that the Republican bosses were against him, and without their machine and money, he could not hope to win the nomination.

This was not the case, but he was caught in the unhappy compromise of convincing voters that their rights were paramount, while at the same time seeking the support of the business community he had so recently punished. In spite of his personal uncertainties, his nomination was as sure as the coming of winter. Even the *Wall Street Journal* could find nothing wrong with his third Message to Congress that December.

Since there was no significant opposition to the President, the Republican convention in June, 1904, could not have been duller. The campaign which followed was indifferent. The nominee could not participate, and he was the party's most colorful asset.

On Election Day, Theodore and Edith went up to Oyster Bay to vote. By the time they returned to Washington, it was obvious he was winning. Because they were tense with waiting, Alice and Ted had done nothing all day but insult each other. When they saw their father

enter the White House, they ran to meet him with the news that Buffalo had given him a sweeping majority. That was typical of what was happening all over the country. For the first time since the Civil War, the South split its loyalties. Even Missouri contributed to the victory. A victory that was spelled out unmistakably by

336 electoral votes (the Democratic candidate received 140) and a popular vote of 7,628,324!

Theodore was President in his own right. The landslide vote confirmed his record.

Inauguration Day dawned fair, a good omen to politicians. The President greeted congratulating friends with confidence and buoyancy. He slapped them on the back, crushed their hands, laughed at their victory jokes. On the way to the Capitol, he stood in his carriage, waving to the cheering thousands who swarmed the streets. But when he took the oath of office, he was solemn, and the dignity which he assumed or shed as easily as an old coat, was impressive. He was growing stout at forty-seven, and the adolescent merriment that once bubbled in his expression had vanished. His dedication to the highest office in the land was aging Theodore.

The Inaugural Parade which swept down Pennsylvania Avenue that day differed from previous ones. Among the marchers were the miners in their miners' caps; there was a large group of Harvard under-graduates; there were Rough Riders, who had turned Washington upside down, tying their horses to lamp-posts, or racing along sedate avenues, their yip-yips startling pedestrians.

There is a story of how they approached the Presidential stand that March 5th in full gallop, giving the cowboy yells and whoops Roosevelt dearly loved. Just as they saluted the President, one of the Rough Riders threw a lariat around a bystander and dragged him off in tow. Later, when the parade was over, the group rode to the White House. On the steps under the portico, the President waited. Each man rode up, leaned from his saddle and shook hands with his Colonel. The day belonged to Theodore Roosevelt.

23

In his inaugural address Roosevelt said: "Toward all other nations, large and small, our attitude must be one of cordial and sincere friendship. We must show not only in our words but in our deeds that we are earnestly desirous of securing good will by acting toward them in a spirit of just and generous recognition of their rights. But justice and generosity in a nation, as in an individual, count most when shown not by the weak but by the strong."

Contrary to the view of The Old Guard in his own party, the President, with foresight, wanted the United States to be a member of the family of nations. He believed its isolation and self-sufficiency belonged to the past, just as he believed the imperialism of other countries was out-dated and would not be tolerated for long. Both Russia and Japan were ambitious in ways that alarmed him. The Japanese had attacked the Russian fleet off Port Arthur, the latest provocative act in a long-standing quarrel. If either nation dominated the Pacific, the interests of the U.S. in the Far East would be endangered. It was quite possible that in defending these interests America might be drawn into war. Roosevelt was eager for Russia and Japan to negotiate their differences for that reason, of course, and in the cause of world peace.

Prior to this time, his critics had accused him of jingoism, of war-mongering. Now, he threw himself into the role of peacemaker. Both attitudes were reflected in an African proverb he quoted often, "Speak softly and carry a big stick, you will go far."

On June 8, 1905, he wrote to the warring nations, Russia and Japan, pleading with them to negotiate a peace for the sake of the whole world as well as for themselves. The response was hopeful, and it was finally decided that a peace council would be held in the United States, with the President acting as mediator. His first step was to bring together the representatives of both countries on board the presidential yacht, the *Mayflower*. Roosevelt arrived first, making the trip from Sagamore to the yacht anchored in Oyster Bay in time for lunch. It was a cloudless August day, with a breeze whipping the flags of Japan, Russia and the U.S. Besides the *Mayflower*, The *Sylph*, and The *Galveston* on hand to give a twenty-one gun salute to the President, there were the U.S.S. *Tacoma* bringing the Japanese delegation, and the U.S.S. *Chattanooga* bringing the Russians. Assistant Secretary of State, Robert H. D. Pierce, introduced the Russians to the President. The President in turn introduced the Russians to the Japanese. It was a first meeting for the hostile envoys, Baron Komura and Minister Takahira, Count Witte and Baron Rosen.

"Baron Komura, I have the honor to present to you Mr. Witte and Baron Rosen," the President said. Everyone began bowing ceremoniously and courteous conversation filled the frigid silence. To avoid problems of protocol, Roosevelt had ordered a simple buffet lunch. After his guests had served their own plates, he took them to a settee in the corner of the salon, chatting casually all the while. Then he stood to make a toast. How would he handle it? Would it be to the Czar? To the Emperor? to neither?

"Gentlemen . . . " he began, "to the welfare and prosperity of the sovereigns and the peoples of the two great nations whose representatives have met one another on this ship. It is my most earnest hope and prayer in the interest of not only these two great powers, but of all civilized mankind, that a just and lasting peace may speedily be concluded between them."

Observers said that the envoys relaxed after that and even shook hands warmly as they parted, promising to meet in Portsmouth, New Hampshire, a few days later.

The President must have gone to bed that Sunday night with a sense of satisfaction. He had been anxious about the meeting, and the slightest misstep could have ended it in abrupt failure. He had brought it off without a suggestion of partiality for either side; he had put the envoys in contact with one another in a friendly atmosphere, and had left them on their mettle to reach a reasonable agreement. But Roosevelt was realist enough not to be overly encouraged. He knew negotiations would take time and further prodding from him.

During the twenty days that followed the Portsmouth conference, many proposals were made. Most of them were rejected. The talks lagged and broke down. The President got them going again. He wrote to the Czar and to the Emperor in an attempt to restore harmony. He invited first Komura and then Baron Rosen to Sagamore. He showed remarkable sympathy and patience toward both, when what he really wanted to do was "knock their heads together." At one point he told a friend he wished he could push the whole Russian delegation down Cooper's Bluff and drown them. But on August 29, just as it seemed the conference would end up a blind alley, Roosevelt persuaded the envoys to consider one more compromise. With huge relief he later received a phone call from Portsmouth saying the compromise had worked; a peace treaty was being drawn up. From that moment calls and telegrams from all over the world poured into the summer White House praising the President's diplomatic triumph. The press hailed him as "the

most important figure in international statesmanship."
Baron Rosen declared him to be, "one of the most powerful personalities now alive in the whole world."

Quite a coup for a man who had been accused of
being impetuous and rude. In this case, he demonstrated
tactfulness and self-control to a creative degree and was
awarded the Nobel Prize for it.

In that year of 1905 it is possible that Roosevelt's
prestige impressed foreign rulers more than it did the
Senators in his own Congress. "There are several emi-
nent statesmen at the other end of Pennsylvania Avenue
whom I would gladly lend to the Russian government, if
they care to expend them as bodyguards for Grand
Dukes . . . " he complained.

The House opposed his railroad legislation, his proposal to admit Arizona and New Mexico to statehood,
and the much needed pure food bills he had introduced.
It rejected his treaty with Santo Domingo. And, most
important perhaps, it ignored his pleas for economy. The
Congressmen embarrassed him by appropriating such
excessive amounts that there was bound to be a deficit at
the end of the year. About the only presidential proposal
with which the congressmen cooperated was a plan for
strengthening the fleet. (They actually voted to build
two new battleships.) What the President considered
most important to his programs, The Old Guard in his
own party scuttled.

The country was intoxicated with progress and prosperity. For the first time, ships were equipped with wire-
less apparatus; radio and moving pictures were being
tried; concrete was the newest construction material;
airplanes and submarines were in the development stage;
the stock market was heady with speculation and over-
confidence.

For the most part, the Congress was as complacent

and smug as the public, but Roosevelt was worried. He worked harder than ever. In addition to her constant fear of his being assassinated, Edith must now find a way to get him to rest. Even at Sagamore he kept up a rip-roaring pace. By nine in the morning he had exercised the horses, finished breakfast and read an incredible number of newspapers, magazines and letters. Then he plunged into dictation with his secretary. (He wrote to everyone! To any of the children away from home he wrote almost every day.) He talked his way through lunch with politicians, diplomats, writers, artists, reporters, cousins, cowboys, sisters and friends — talked on a startling number of subjects, from the Bible to French military tradition, his mind spilling knowledge that astonished even the experts. Whether friend or foe, Theodore had a way of putting each guest at ease, drawing out an opinion as though it were all-important to him.

It was Edith who remembered the visitor who had contributed something to the discussions or who had gone away disgruntled. She kept a finger on the pulse of public opinion, and she was a much better judge of people than Theodore, sensitive to motives, unfailing in analyzing character. A good thing too, because she was able to keep her husband from falling into many of the traps laid for him. She was always at his side, unobtrusive and reserved. Some observers mistook the reserve for timidity and underestimated her enormous influence over Theodore. Because she preferred privacy to partying, certain society matrons were spiteful. "The President's wife reportedly spends $300 a year on her wardrobe," one said, "and it certainly looks like it." But the Roosevelts, determined to be themselves, laughed at criticism. With utter naturalness they were at once simple and spectacular.

No one was left unimpressed by the President's extravagant vitality. He was "an interesting combination of St. Vitus and St. Paul," according to a British visitor, who went on to say that the two most wonderful things he had seen in the United States were Niagara Falls and the President, "both great wonders of nature!"

Conferences continued through the afternoon and dinner hour. It was not uncommon for Theodore to excuse himself and race a pack of children down Cooper's Bluff for a swim, or take Edith for a seven mile row. If he was in Washington, he was likely to take off a couple of hours for football or ju jitsu. Cross-country hiking was a favorite exercise, which may explain his good health while in office in spite of doing the work of several men. On these hikes he took along officials and friends for a "try-out." If they couldn't keep up with him as he ran through the park, up and down the banks of Rock Creek, climbing over all obstacles, he did not consider them fit. One general was "promoted" to a desk job because he could not "endure." It was not in jest that the men who worked most closely with him were dubbed the "Tennis Cabinet" — they had proved their fitness beyond any doubt.

Such robust activity made him popular with children, but there was a still more important reason they were always inviting him to share their fun — he did not talk down to them; he treated them as equals; he was humorous and entertaining.

With his own family he was never too busy for a pillow fight at bedtime followed by quiet moments of reading and prayers. It is to his credit that the Roosevelt children grew up relishing these times as much as they did the active, sports-filled hours.

When they were at Oyster Bay, they attended the little village Episcopal church; when in Washington, St.

John's across the square from the White House, or Grace Reformed church. Regular attendance at worship and daily Bible reading were as much a part of life as politics, because Theodore's faith in God was a practical, every day matter, not reserved for Sundays only.

Quentin, being the youngest, may have gotten away with more pranks than his older brothers and sisters. He was leader of a gang of boys that gained fame in the Capitol as the "White House Gang." Quentin had his father's originality, boldness and initiative. His hair was usually mussed, his tie askew, his socks falling down, his trousers torn — "a roly-poly-happy-go-lucky personage," in Theodore's words, "the brightest of any of the children but with a strong tendency to pass a very happy life in doing absolutely nothing except swim or loaf with other little boys."

One day Quentin's gang was riding on a Washington trolley car, making fierce faces out the windows at passersby, when along came the President in an open carriage. The boys did their worst, and the President grimaced back at them just as ferociously. As the trolley and carriage stopped alongside in the traffic, he called loud enough for everyone around to hear, "I was thinking of asking you to ride the rest of the way with me — Quentin and friends — but it's really too dangerous for me to be seen with you."

Wherever the family was staying, pets were in abundance. To mention a few, there were Slipper, a cat; Bill, the lizard; Tom Quartz, the kitten; a King snake, and assorted "little wee" snakes; horses, horses, horses, dogs — Black Jack, Ace, Skip, Brier, Mike, Scamp; Maude, a white pig; a badger, five guinea pigs, and a small bear named Jonathan Edwards!

24

Toward the end of Roosevelt's second term in office, he was particularly proud of the progress that had been made in two projects. One was the Reclamation Act, the other was the Conservation movement. Twenty-eight reclamation plans had been carried out to provide irrigation for more than 3,000,000 acres of farmland. This did much to convince the nation that it could manage its own resources, and it brought stability to the arid west.

The area of the National Forests was increased from 43,000,000 acres to 194,000,000, trained forestry technicians from 500 men to 3,000. For the first time, fire prevention became a matter of public conscience. 51 Bird Reservations were established, and all wildlife came under protective regulations. The President considered the report of the National Conservation Commission to Congress "one of the most fundamentally important documents every laid before the American people." Up until then, he had done more than any other person to make the country recognize its natural resources. We owe him much for initiating measures to conserve those resources and for his vision, which is a reality in our national park system today. Time has proved the wisdom of his foresight.

Internationally, progress was more limited. There were rumbles of war in the Pacific and in Europe. One incident was alarmingly significant to Roosevelt. A reporter of the New York *Times* had shown him notes taken during an interview with the German Kaiser.

"You must not print this!" growled the President.

"He's threatening war with England and baldly states we are preparing to fight Japan. This jack of an Emperor is psychopathic!"

It was plain that the Kaiser was trying to stir up hostilities. In former dealings with him, Theodore had discovered that the only thing the German ruler respected was force. How could he impress him and the Japanese that America wanted peace, but peace through strength?

An unhappy situation had arisen in California from a large migration of Japanese who provided cheap labor. Certain bigoted agitators in the state were urging citizens to exclude Japanese children from the schools and abusive language was being used by reporters covering the crisis.

In his characteristic way, the President sent for the political leaders of California for a face-to-face review of the problems. His own view was made very clear: "All relations between the two peoples must be those of reciprocal justice. It is an intolerant outrage on the part of newspapers and public men to use offensive and insulting language about a high-spirited sensitive, friendly people." Under Roosevelt, even the rights of the Japanese would be protected.

Temporarily tensions were relieved, but rumors continued to leak to the White House that Japan was planning to attack the Philippines. By August of 1907, the President had decided to act. He sent as his personal envoy, the Secretary of War, William Howard Taft, to Tokyo and Yokohama. Taft talked with all of the leading officials there. In two months he cabled the President that the Kaiser was inciting misunderstanding; the Japanese were eager to avoid war. That cable cost $1,500, and it was worth it. Roosevelt ordered the fleet of 16 battleships and their crews of 12,000 men on a trip around the world to display the might of the U.S. What could have been more timely and dramatic?

Numerous critics of the President's decision, including German naval experts as well as Americans, predicted that the sailing of the fleet would bring on war. Instead, the Japanese government invited the fleet to visit their shores for three days of Oriental hospitality. Suddenly, once more, Theodore Roosevelt was heralded as a peace-maker, and his favorite branch of the military, the navy, was capturing international attention.

While the navy was on everyone's mind, the President asked the Congress for four more battleships. Congress reluctantly authorized two. Roosevelt had anticipated this, "I knew I wouldn't get two unless I asked for four."

He received something more personal than ships and goodwill from his peace scheme. He acquired a son-in-law. In the party of distinguished Americans accompanying Secretary of War Taft to Japan, was Alice. She was always newsworthy on her own, but the press was delighted to learn that one of Alice's gentlemen friends was also in the party. He was Ohio congressman, Nicholas Longworth, considered the most eligible bachelor in Washington. No one was surprised when the Roosevelts announced the engagement of Alice and Nick a few weeks after their return from the Orient. The wedding, one sunny Saturday in February, was the most glamorous affair to take place in the White House since Nellie Grant's marriage. On that romantic occasion, "Princess Alice" stole the limelight from her famous father. Only she could have done it.

25

The more Roosevelt accomplished in the Presidency, the more the pressure mounted for him to run again in 1908. It was pressure from the grass-roots this time. He had traveled more and met more people than any previous President. The common folk felt at home with him. He had protected their rights. The Square Deal was their creed. And they wanted to "keep Teddy!" Oddly enough, the nickname "Teddy" was now a byword all over the world, but Roosevelt never liked the name, and people who knew him well did not use it. (He liked to be known as "T.R.")

But the average citizens did not need to know him well to love him. People used the nickname and the informal initials as they would terms of affection. Why shouldn't "Teddy" go right on doing the good job he was doing?

Not everyone knew that on Inauguration Day, four years before, he had flatly stated he would not run for a third term. He felt that he wanted to follow the precedent set by George Washington. "I believe in power," he said, "but I believe that responsibility should go with power, and that it is not well that the strong executive should be a perpetual executive."

Politicians do not always keep pledges; Roosevelt could have rationalized his. It could not have been an easy decision for him to turn down the demands of the American voters. He admitted he enjoyed being President. For seven years he had ridden astride the job with success and growing popularity, and there was much more to accomplish. But he did not allow himself to be tempted. He instructed his friend Lodge, who would be permanent chairman for the Republican National Convention, that he would not accept nomination, and wrote a letter of refusal in case there was need for it. He let it be known through the press that he was planning a hunting trip in Africa. He would leave as soon as the new President was inaugurated. In this way his successor would be unhampered even by his presence in the country.

Who would be the new President? It was more or less for Roosevelt to say. He suggested the office to Elihu Root, who was not interested. Then to Justice Charles Evans Hughes. He was too independent to accept a favor from T.R. Others were undoubtedly considered, but there was only one man he was certain would carry on his policies, who shared his philosophy of government. That man was William Howard Taft. Taft, Roosevelt knew, could carry the Convention and the election.

Taft won the November election. Roosevelt's choice was proved a popular one, and in March 1909, he left the Presidency at the height of his power. Even the political cynics and manipulators on Capitol Hill found it hard to say good-by, and several members of the "Tennis Cabinet," his finest friends, wept.

1909 - 1919

PART FOUR

26

There were two reasons behind Roosevelt's decision to go to Africa for a big game hunting trip. The first and most obvious — he was tired. The years of responsibility and incessant activity had sapped him of his old vitality. He was still bothered by a fever he had contracted in Cuba. In one of his regular boxing bouts in the White House gymnasium, he had lost the sight of his left eye, although this was not known by the public. He was definitely overweight for a man of fifty. It was time he relaxed from people and work. What better way than to go on safari in the African wilds?

The second reason for the trip is more significant, because it reveals a sensitivity all too rare in politicians. T. R. did not want to cast a shadow over Taft's administration. If he stayed at home the press would be constantly quoting his opinions, and his friends in government would pressure him for backing. In no time it would seem that the President and ex-President were in competition. He believed this was an unfair burden to add to the one Taft had assumed in the Presidency.

Edith did not want her husband to make the trip, and she was not the only one who tried to dissuade him. Almost everyone close to him was opposed to it, fearing he would be killed by deadly disease or wild animals. Of course, his enemies were glad to see him go. As his term ended, their hatred had become more intense and eloquent. They used words to describe him such as ogre, insane, monster, violent, egotist. They were openly hopeful he would not return from Africa. A toast often repeated by the wealthy in their clubs and by bitter congressmen in their saloons was, "Health to the lions!"

As Theodore embodied strong contradictions in his personality, so did the times. Extremes dominated politics, the arts, architecture, religion, the economy. The younger generation, typified by Alice, was frivolous and pleasure-loving. They sang popular hits with trifling lyrics — "Only a Bird in a Gilded Cage" and "Wal, I Swan, I Must Be Gettin' On." Their parents criticized the new President for playing the "aristocratic" game of golf. And the number one pastime in Washington was going over to Fort Meyer to watch the Wright brothers fly. If there was a breeze, the flight was called off. If weather was ideal, the flying machine would ascend to the awesome height of 100 feet and circle the field, while the watching crowd gasped in dizzy disbelief.

When Roosevelt sailed from Hoboken on March 23, 1909, in the S.S. *Hamburg* with his twenty-year-old son, Kermit, Edith and the rest of the family were not among the throng who waved farewell. They had remained at Sagamore. And so T.R. was free to shake hands with admirers right up until the last minute. The Rough Riders were there, and President Taft's aide who brought a parting gift. A cornetist played "There'll Be a Hot Time in the Old Town Tonight," and Colonel Roosevelt steamed off happily toward another kind of adventure.

Before he was old enough to read, the child Theodore's favorite book had been one almost too large for him to carry. It was the life story of Dr. David Livingstone, the great explorer and missionary who first wrote back to the civilized world about the Dark Continent, Africa. Theodore must have thought of his hero Livingstone when he landed at Mombassa with his large party of hunters, taxidermists, porters, guides and servants.

Kermit liked camping and hunting as much as his father, who wrote home that the boy was too reckless, but he may have been imitating his parent. They would travel for days into desolate wilderness inhabited only by wild animals. The howls of hyenas and lions split the tropical night, while the faithful black attendants chanted around the campfire.

In lion country, the natives, armed with bows and arrows, went ahead to beat the bush, frightening the king of the jungle from his lair. Then followed the dogs and gunbearers, each cautious and ready for action, because a lion moves so quickly, a hunter may not have time to reload his gun after a shot. T.R. usually began shooting from a distance of 150 yards. As the beast came toward him, he shot it first in the chest, then in the withers as the lion turned away, and finally in the back, breaking the vertebrae.

His first encounter with a lion was almost his last. He and Kermit on horseback, began a chase across an open stretch, but after a time Theodore found himself separated from rest of the party except for one guide who stuck with him. As the two men galloped after the fleeing lion, it turned suddenly and charged them. There was only one thing to do — rein in the horses, dismount and gamble on getting a good shot.

"Use my shoulder for support, Colonel," shouted the guide, crouching between the horses. Roosevelt propped his elbow on the guide's shoulder to steady his aim and squeezed the trigger.

"Got him!" he shouted as the lion toppled over a few yards away. But the lion was far from dead. "He's wounded, Colonel, but he's getting up," the guide warned. "Reload, sir! Here he comes again!" With cool courage and steady nerve, the Colonel took aim again. The lion was in a position to spring, but he waited an instant too long. T.R. fired just as the lion reared back on his haunches to leap.

"Right through the belly, sir, and the backbone!"

"A bully shot!" Roosevelt said, as excited as a small boy scoring a bull's eye. Without hesitating, he rushed to the fallen lion and began measuring it from nose to tip of tail.

The guide stood up and wiped the perspiration from the back of his neck. "I hope you is always this lucky, Colonel," he said.

The adventures of the African hunt fill a book written by Roosevelt called, *African Game Trails.* There was more than that one lion to conquer; there were savage rhinos, infuriated elephants, bone-crushing pythons, wounded hippopotamuses, raging fever, the relentless heat, and a near-fatal brush with sleeping sickness.

The Colonel survived them all. By the end of the year, he had sent back to the Smithsonian Institute over 6,000 skins and hides, rare birds, fish, reptiles, specimen plants and flowers, primitive utensils and tools. No expedition had ever produced such bounty. He was ready to quit the trail and return to civilization.

Christmas away from home was harder to bear than any of the safari hardships. In a letter to Ethel, he wrote, "I am so eagerly looking forward to the end, when I shall see darling, pretty Mother, my own sweetheart, and the very nicest of all nice daughters . . . " He also bragged about the skill Kermit had developed as a hunter and the efficient way his son had directed the whole caravan. The best compliment was, "He is also the nicest possible companion."

In March of 1910, the party sailed down the White

Nile to Khartoum, where Edith and Ethel were waiting. It was a dramatic reunion after a year of separation. Having trekked over 1,000 miles through jungles, T.R. expected the rest of the tour to be safe and comfortable.

He especially enjoyed one stop made at the invitation of the African Inland Mission, where he laid a foundation stone for a mission building in the Rift Valley. Long afterward, the missionaries remembered the way he praised their unselfish efforts. As usual, he also had some advice: "The white man in Africa can be permanently successful only if he tries to help and understand the native. . . . Be such a Christian that anybody who sees you will know that your religion is second to none."

As had been the case all of his life, even in Africa, T.R. showed a remarkable knack for fitting in with all classes of people. More than ever, he abhorred intolerance and bigotry. At the risk of being misunderstood by the Protestant majority in America, he said of a Catholic missionary at Kampala, "Mother Paul is the strongest character I've met in Central Africa!"

27

From Khartoum the Roosevelts went to Egypt; from Egypt to Italy. Everywhere crowds gathered to get a glimpse of the Colonel and to welcome the returning hero. While in Rome, Theodore hired a carriage to take Edith over the same route they had followed on their honeymoon twenty-four years before. He had not changed. He was the same sentimental, romantic lover, and all of the kings and rulers in Europe could wait while he spent a few quiet, private days with Edith.

In Vienna, Emperor Franz Josef honored the former President with an intimate conference such as was usually reserved only for royalty. T.R. was cordial, but he obviously enjoyed much more a visit to the riding school where the celebrated Lippizzan breed of horses was shown him in a special exhibition. The perfectly trained Lippizzans did dainty turns, danced the quadrille and finally came onto the platform where the Roosevelts were seated, circling so near their chairs, their hoofs almost brushed Edith's feet.

A tremendous ovation greeted Theodore in Budapest, Hungary. From there he went to Paris, where a carefully arranged line of dignitaries waited for the train to pull in. Splendid in full-dress uniforms or cut-aways and silk hats, they were startled to see the tanned and beaming face of T.R. as he leaned far out the window of his car, shouting heartily at the American Ambassador, Robert Bacon, who also stood in line.

"Bob, we're here! How are you?" he boomed. The line broke and ceremony was forgotten as everyone ran to the train window. "Isn't this bully?" Theodore said, slapping Ambassador Bacon on the back. "And here's Baron Takahira, my old friend!" While the French dignitaries gaped, T.R. reached down and lifted the little Japanese official off his feet.

That was the beginning of a reception unlike any Paris had witnessed before. At last Roosevelt emerged onto the station platform, his black felt hat jammed shapelessly on his head, his overcoat rumpled. As he drove to the American embassy on that soft, silvery spring morning, thousands of Parisians lined the avenues and cheered.

Paris was accustomed to visiting celebrities, but this one was unique. The evening paper said, "No democratic chief of state ever before enjoyed such popularity. It is the man, not the office being honored. It is his vigor, his personality, his character, ideas and temperament which appeal to European opinion."

Theodore later wrote about the important events during the Paris visit, and he also noted minor details that amused him, such as the prices of fruit listed on the menu at an elaborate dinner given for him at the Elysian palace — "Very Large Strawberries (30 cents each); Peaches ($3.00 each); Hot House Grapes ($7.00 a bunch)"

The Parisians would not forget the speech he gave at the Sorbonne. He was expected to wear the green brocaded robes of an academician. Instead, he walked briskly to the lectern in his far from new frock coat. Every seat was taken, and he waited for some minutes for the welcoming applause to end. The speech is well worth reading today.

" . . . Success or failure will be conditioned upon the way in which the *average* man, the *average* woman, does his or her duty . . . in the *ordinary* everyday affairs of life . . . "

" . . . the main source of national power and national greatness is found in the *average* citizenship of the nation . . . "

" . . . There is little use for the being whose tepid soul knows nothing of the great and generous emotion, of the high pride, the stern belief, the lofty enthusiasm of the men who quell the storm and ride the thunder . . . "

" . . . It is a bad thing for a nation to raise and to admire a false standard of success; and there can be no falser standard than that set by deification of material wellbeing in and for itself. . . . "

Belgium — Holland — the crowds grew still larger. Amsterdam welcomed Roosevelt with personal pride, and naturally he boasted of his Dutch ancestry: "I am visiting the country from which my people came three centuries ago." There, the celebrations were doubled since the city was illuminated in honor of the second birthday of Princess Juliana.

The only time Theodore escaped the public was when he went to the Ryks museum to look at Rembrandt's masterpieces. The gallery was quiet; the great man could be alone with his thoughts and the profound beauty of Holland's genius.

The Danish Court was known to be highly formal. Respecting this, T.R. was embarrassed upon arriving in Copenhagen to learn that his baggage was missing. He had no choice but to attend the dinner given in his honor by Prince Christian in his plain gray travel suit. Far from being offended, the Prince seemed pleased. So were the other important guests around the table. Who cared how the most popular big game hunter in the world was dressed?

In Norway, even the King and Queen were very democratic, which was a relief after all the splendor and ceremony and protocol to which Theodore had been exposed. Kings certainly did not dazzle him. "... They are expected to be a kind of sublimated American Vice President," he observed. "I cannot imagine a more appallingly dreary life ... "

He confided to the Norwegian king that this kind of trip was harder than campaigning for election. He felt "most at home" with the Crown Prince, whom the Norwegians affectionately called "small Olaf." He was as full of mischief as Quentin and as ready to play games with the American ex-President.

"Be sure you read Heims Kringle to small Olaf," Theodore advised the Queen. That was his own favorite of the classic Norwegian sagas. Just as freely he gave advice to the Nobel Prize Committee: "We need to form a league of peace with enough military power behind it to insure peace in today's world." This suggestion received little notice in 1910. Eight years later, when it was repeated by Woodrow Wilson it became a number one news story.

From Norway, T.R. went by special train to Sweden where he was greeted with the sad news that King Edward of England was dead. But the visit to Sweden was "dee-lightful!"

The next stop was Berlin, and the press, along with the American Ambassador, wondered how the Kaiser would receive the man who had met German threats with strength and fearlessness. The Kaiser surprised everyone by inviting T.R. to special military maneuvers staged exclusively for him. Afterward, the Kaiser said, "My friend Roosevelt, I have been greatly pleased to show

127

you some of our troops. You are the first civilian to review them."

Contrary to what observers had hinted, the Kaiser had not been offended when the two leaders met, even though Roosevelt had substituted a vigorous handshake for the deep bow which German etiquette dictated. On the back of a picture taken on that occasion, the Kaiser wrote, "When we shake hands, we shake the world."

The Berlin greeting had been loud and colorful, but when T.R.'s party reached Victoria Station, London, the crowd stood silent and serious. The platform was draped in royal purple, and even the delegation of Boy Scouts wore black mourning bands around their gray felt hats. The Roosevelts were somber as they entered the carriage of the American Ambassador. The people pushed near to look at the party, but they spoke in hushed tones. Their king was dead.

"T.R. looks a lot smaller than I expected," one Londoner said to another. When speaking from a platform T.R. looked massive and tall. He was actually five feet, eight inches in height which was a surprise to those who stood close to him for the first time.

The Union Jacks at half mast along the route from the station reminded him that he was not in London to be entertained. Rather, his was the solemn role of America's special representative to the funeral of the British monarch.

Still, during the four weeks that followed, there were bright times in England too. When he went to Cambridge University to receive an honorary degree, the undergraduates let down a huge teddy bear from the ceiling as soon as the degree was conferred. And at Oxford, they sang, "For He's a Jolly Good Fellow."

In London's Guildhall, T.R. made a speech which was frankly critical of England's colonial policy. This inspired a cartoon of him standing on the tail of a lion representing Britain. On the lion's face was an expression of anguish. Another cartoonist drew the famous lions of Trafalgar Square being guarded by London bobbies. Nearby a sign read: "These lions are not to be shot."

Alice joined her father and mother, Ethel and Kermit in London and sailed with them to the States.

Since his return from the African wilds, Roosevelt had been feted and honored as no other world figure of that time. As the ship, *Kaiserin Auguste Victoria,* hung with hundreds of flags, entered New York harbor, Alice stood proudly beside her father on the captain's bridge. Battleships, destroyers and small craft formed an escort, their whistles shrieking. Vast crowds cheered from the Battery. A 21-gun salute, usually fired only for the President in office, echoed across the water. A cutter drew alongside with Ted and Quentin and Archie aboard, waving wildly. Theodore was home again. It had been the trip of a lifetime, but nothing he had experienced compared with being back with his family and (his larger family) the American people. They roared their greeting as he stepped briskly down the gangplank. For five minutes the shout and applause went up, "Hurrah for Teddy!" It was not the mist of the gray June morning that Theodore wiped from his eyes. He was just as happy to be back with the people as they were to have him.

There had to be a little speech-making, of course, from a stand hung with red, white and blue bunting. It all seemed so familiar, as though he had not been away. He said he was "ready and eager" to serve the people in any way they needed him. For T.R. it was a remarkably

129

brief speech. In a letter written some days before, he had promised President Taft, "I shall make no speeches or say anything for two months, but I shall keep my mind as open as I keep my mouth shut." Nevertheless, politicians wondering what effect his return would have on Taft, questioned what Roosevelt meant by "ready and eager." Was he going to return to public life?

The parade up Broadway was led by a troop of Rough Riders in sharply creased new uniforms. As the returning hero's carriage inched through the mass of cheering citizens, the former President stood, waved, bowing to the left, to the right, genuinely humbled by the triumphant reception.

At the same time, he knew how quickly praise could be turned to scorn and rejection. History proved that; over and over again it had happened to famous men. He wondered how long this favorable mood toward him would last — until tomorrow, until next week?

No one would have guessed his uncertainties could they have watched him the following evening, rocking on the west piazza at Sagamore. Oh, it was good to be in this dear place, with Edith beside him, watching the sunset fade over the Sound. They counted the bird calls the way they always had — thrush, vireo, tanager, ovenbird. An oriole sang in the weeping elm, and catbirds fussed with sparrows in the hedges. Why not settle for this tranquility for the rest of his life?

For days he had been receiving messages from men in government bringing him up to date on the affairs of the Republican party and the administration of Taft. Things were very different that June from what they were when he left the preceding year. The country was astir with unrest and dissatisfaction. Taft had failed to keep the party united. The more he appeared to favor

The Old Guard or Conservatives, the more the progressive wing, The Insurgents, split away in the opposite direction.

Inevitably, reporters began arriving at Sagamore to get Colonel Roosevelt's views on the fight. He protested that he had no statements. "The one thing I want now is privacy," he said. Well, he was not a hypocrite. One of his bitterest critics said T.R. did not have a dishonest bone in his body. But he *was* human, and he was plagued by the impulses that men of power act upon. These impulses are sometimes contradictory.

Within four days after returning, Theodore broke his pledge to keep his mouth shut. Within ten days, two of Taft's most influential foes, Gifford Pinchot and Senator LaFollette of Wisconsin, were entertained at Sagamore. A stream of party rebels and reporters followed. The hours were filled with appointments — the hours Theodore had promised himself to keep uninterrupted. When Taft heard that his foes and the ex-President had been in conference, he concluded he had been betrayed. The result was a permanent misunderstanding between the two great Republicans.

At about the same time, the New York *World* predicted that Roosevelt would be a candidate for President in 1912.

In the fall of 1910 this certainly did not seem likely as elections on the state level indicated that the voters were weary of Republican administration. New York went Democratic, and New Jersey elected Woodrow Wilson governor.

When a reporter asked T.R. if this was an indication he should relax and stay out of the political battle, the Colonel replied that he could not live with himself if he did not do all he could for the party. In defeat, it might need him more than ever. Did he have a secret conviction that he could provide the leadership that would put the party back in power? Or was the boredom of retirement impossible to face? He only knew he could not be a spectator; he must participate in public affairs. He also knew that he did not want to be President again. With candor he wrote, "I think the American people feel a little tired of me, a feeling with which I cordially sympathize."

28

In the months that followed, T.R. became convinced that the Taft administration was marching straight to defeat. And while he, himself, was asking his friends not to pressure him into the national picture, he was very definitely influencing public opinion through articles in the *Outlook* and in speeches he continued to make whenever there was opportunity. His cause had been given a new label. Instead of the Square Deal, he now preached the New Nationalism. Progressives and rebels were following his lead away from the conservative principles of Taft, whom they accused of serving the "special interests" of Wall Street. In their opinion, Taft had sold out to the party's old enemies, the wealthy dictators in big business. It may have been a reckless charge, but it rallied many followers to Roosevelt's old banner, "Fight for the underdog!"

In February, 1912, a petition signed by seven governors was published. It included a history of the Progressive movement, and it declared that only T.R. could lead it to victory. Taft called the drafters of this petition "emotionalists or neurotics, who have lost their sense of proportion. . . . " Whether Taft's reaction led to Roosevelt's decision is not known, but immediately T.R. coined a new phrase, declaring, "My hat is in the ring!"

Most of his former colleagues in government were dismayed. They figured that if he could only wait until 1916, he would get the Republican nomination without splitting the party. But his impatience to "be in the saddle again" outran his normally keen political sense, and he struck out to win public support without any party machinery to back him. The battle that ensued was so violent that Alice hurried to his side just to stand by him. As Theodore himself put it, " . . . all respectable society is now apoplectic with rage over me. Literally, I have no supporters of prominence in the east. . . . " He had embarked on a dangerous course, independent of accepted political logic, and he would stubbornly hold to it.

When the Republican National Committee met in Chicago, it was predetermined that Taft would be the nominee of the convention, even though the rank and file majority was for T.R. In the first vote taken, 561 ballots were cast for Taft, 107 for Roosevelt. 344 delegates did not vote, which was taken as an indication that a third party would receive substantial support. At a special meeting called in Chicago's Orchestra Hall, the 344 non-voting delegates decided there was no other way to stop the G.O.P. machine — they would form an independent party.

Funds would have to be raised, a convention called, a nominee selected since this splinter group had none of the state organizations behind it. On August 5, 1912, the first convention of the Progressive Party opened in Chicago. Was it to be the only real hope of America? Had both of the old parties failed? Could the Progressives end poverty and unemployment and depressions the way they claimed? The 10,000 people attending seemingly had no doubts. At last, they believed, there would be a political organization that would solve all of America's problems, and its leader would be none other than Theodore Roosevelt, the "Bull Moose."

The crowd adjourned from the first Progressive convention singing hymns. In fact, "Onward Christian Soldiers" became the battle song. Heading the crusade was their hero who promised to make a "holy fight for the people and the Lord."

Claiming the Almighty for an ally, loud singing and camp meeting fervor did not drown out the undercurrent of defeat. "My public career will probably end on Election Day," T.R. told a Philadelphia publisher. "But I've got to make the fight."

Immediately the exhausting grind of campaigning began. He was older now, and it wore on him. The miles of travel, the crowds, the irregular meals, the endless speech-making, the local politicians demanding that he settle all quarrels, the press expecting colorful copy day after day — it all tired him now. After touring the South and parts of the Middle West, his throat bothered him so much that several speeches were cancelled. His voice was giving out.

On the other hand, the Democratic nominee was fresh and spirited. This was Woodrow Wilson's first Presidential campaign, and a strong tide was running for his election. He and his supporters were optimistic, confident.

On the spur of the moment, Alice decided to take a train to Chicago to hear one of her father's major speeches on October 12. All summer she had tried to persuade T.R.'s former backers in the East to help him. Most of her attempts were in vain. Some of his old friends had stopped speaking to him, and even Cabot Lodge was rather cool. Seeing her father again, surrounded by the loyal men accompanying him on his trip, reassured Alice, and no one was more wildly enthusiastic when the Bull Moose spoke at Chicago's Coliseum. His savage attack on Wilson set the crowd to shouting vengeance.

Alice took the train back to her home in Cincinnati happy for her father's Chicago reception, but she had his political sixth sense, and they were both without any real hope.

The next day, T.R. was scheduled to make a speech in Milwaukee. Alice was back home having dinner with Nick that evening when she read in the paper that her father had been shot as he left the Gilpatrick Hotel to go to the political rally.

"I don't believe it, Nick," was Alice's first comment. "There are so many rumors — about just everything."

"You're probably right, my dear."

But a few minutes later a phone call came through from Chicago, and Nick could not hide the nature of the message as he rejoined Alice at the table.

"It's true, Alice. Some maniac shouting something about a third term, shot your father at close range."

"Is he alive, Nick? That's all that matters."

"Yes, dear, very much so. The crowd was ready to lynch the assassin on the spot, but Mr. Roosevelt ordered them to have mercy on the fellow and allow the police to take him away safely."

Alice smiled faintly. "And they took Father to the hospital?"

"No," Nick hesitated. "No — he has gone on to the hall to speak."

"That's ridiculous!" Alice cried. "Ridiculous and exactly like him! He'll make that speech or die."

T.R. made the speech while members of his party frantically begged him to stop. "I'll do the best I can," the Colonel began, ignoring his advisers. "There is a bullet in my body, but it is nothing . . . our cause is everything! If one soldier who carries our banner is stricken, there will be another to pick it up and carry on!"

Haltingly he delivered the speech, then he was rushed to the emergency room of the Milwaukee Hospital for examination. The bullet had entered his right breast, but its force was spent as it passed through Roosevelt's heavy overcoat, glasses case and the folded manuscript of his address. Such a close brush with death did not daunt him. "Being shot is a trade risk," he said. "A risk which every prominent public man ought to accept as a matter of course."

Edith could not be casual about such a near-fatality. Her anxiety of the years culminated in that instant the shot lodged in Theodore's side. She was brave, and she was grateful for his survival, but she was shaken and white-faced during the days of his convalescence.

29

Before the shooting, a large percentage of voters was indifferent about the campaigning. All three candidates had stooped to such violent attacks on their opponents, and the language had become so exaggerated and rash that many people stopped listening. But the attack on T.R. stirred sympathy for the old Rough Rider. Taft and Wilson sent regrets and agreed to halt the campaign until he was able to speak again. From Sagamore, where he went to rest, the Progressive Candidate announced that he would make only one more address on October 30.

On that date, he arrived at Madison Square Garden looking healthy and cheerful. His supporters jammed the entrances and stampeded for seats — 16,000 of them (another 15,000 could not get inside). When the Colonel strode with his familiar, energetic walk to the platform, an unforgettable demonstration broke loose. The din lasted 41 minutes! It was not a demonstration led by cheerleaders and bands as is the custom at political conventions. This was a spontaneous expression of relief and affection. The band tried to play "The Battle Hymn of the Republic," but it could not be heard above the bedlam.

T.R. was pleased. He was also impatient. Finally, after forty minutes, he pounded the desk for order. Only he could command such a mass of people to silence. But the silence did not last. Almost every sentence of his message was applauded. "Quiet down!" he shouted, shaking his finger warningly. The speech was impressively free of bitter or malicious rantings. " . . . A plea for human rights," one paper called it. "A supplication for equal justice and liberty — a demand for the survival of the American form of government."

The course of the election was not affected. Taft received 8 electoral votes, Roosevelt 88, and Wilson 435. But Wilson's popular vote was only 2,000,000 more than the 4,126,020 votes received by Theodore Roosevelt, who said, "I accept the result with entire good humor."

When a supporter mentioned the possibility of a Progressive victory in 1916, T.R. said, "I thought you were a better politician. The fight is over. We are beaten. There is only one thing to do, and that is to go back to the Republican Party. You can't hold a party like the Progressive Party together . . . there are no loaves and fishes." He had no illusions; he had expected defeat.

If he was depressed during the weeks that followed, it was not because he lost the election, but because he was lonely. There were no reporters driving up the hill to Sagamore, the telephone was quiet, even the Oyster Bay neighbors were withdrawn. To them he was now a "liberal revolutionary." There was nothing left to do but write. And write he did, with his usual whole-hearted passion. He contributed frequently to the Kansas City *Star,* worked on his memoirs and completed a series of books, "Life Histories of African Game Animals." He would devote his time to becoming a scholar, country gentleman and father. Once he faced the fact that he was no longer "at the top," the change must have been restful. At last there was time to enjoy Sagamore, to describe its beauty: "Early in April there is one hillside near us which glows like a tender flame with the white of the bloodroot. About the same time we find the shy mayflower, the trailing arbutus . . . then there are shad-blow and delicate anemones about the time of the cherry blossoms; the brief glory of the apple orchard follows; and then the thronging dogwoods fill the forests with their radiance."

The man who wrote so poetically of the changing seasons, (and who loved, as only a naturalist can, the variety of nature,) was the same man, who as warrior, had raged through a last futile campaign. He could still be as eager and absorbed about a black-throated green warbler, as he had recently been about the direct primary. One of his concerns at this time was the strange disappearance of the whip-poor-wills. "We no longer hear them at night." Like a child, he turned to the simple pleasures of the out of doors and books, and they restored his cheerful spirit. The loneliness and doubt gave way to his old humor and boyish delight, and when Ethel was married to Richard Derby that summer, he welcomed the wedding guests to Sagamore with customary easy hospitality; older, yes, but exuberant and happy.

30

By October, Theodore was ready for another scientific expedition similar to the one made in Africa. This time he accepted an invitation from the Brazilian government to speak on the problems of democracy. Arrangements were also made to collect specimens for New York's American Museum of Natural History. Kermit, who had accompanied him to Africa, went along, and two naturalists from the museum. Edith sailed with them and toured the South American capitals with her husband until it was time for him to begin his expedition, then she returned home.

From January to April, she had no word from him. He had set out with a party of twenty to explore a practically unknown river, the Rio da Duvida, River of Doubt. It flowed through the central jungles of Brazil toward the north where it was said to join the great Amazon.

About half of the party consisted of native pack-carriers and rowers. With dugout canoes and supplies for forty days, they struck out. But in a matter of hours they ran into rapids so treacherous, they knew their canoes could not navigate them. It took over two days to hack a trail through the jungle and bypass the rapids. From that time on, the experience was often repeated. Most of their energy was spent crawling foot by foot through the steaming, insect-infested jungle. The party began losing men and supplies alarmingly. Malaria weakened everyone, including Roosevelt, who had injured a leg as he crossed a stream. Not only did his injury become infected, he was desperately ill with fever. The march was halted when he grew too ill to be carried.

He knew the area was uninhabited. No help could reach this forsaken place. All of the party would be wiped out by fever and hunger if they waited for him to recover, so he begged the other men to leave him. He even thought of killing himself to relieve them from feeding and caring for him.

Kermit refused to go. The others followed young Roosevelt's decision. For two days his father was delirious, then the fever broke — just when there seemed to be no hope. With superhuman effort, T.R. got to his feet and ordered the party forward. When he was carried once more to his dugout, he was too weak to dip a hand in the water to bathe his face.

Soon the river widened. This meant the rapids were at last behind. After two months of punishing struggle, they had reached smooth navigable water. It was with relief, a few days later, that they saw a man gathering rubber from a grove on the river bank. He was their first contact with civilization since the almost disastrous trek began, and the man told them they could board a ship for Manaos, a town on the Amazon.

After months of silence, not knowing whether Theodore and Kermit were alive or dead, Edith received a message in April. They were homeward bound! It took another month for them to reach New York, and even Edith was unprepared for the sight of her husband — the thin, weakened man leaning hard on a cane. The pallor of death was still on Theodore's face, and it mattered little to Edith that he had charted an unexplored river through a thousand miles of Brazilian jungles. Because he was proud, she tried to be, of the honor Brazil gave him by changing the name of the river from The River of Doubt to the Rio Teodoro. But she knew the fever had shortened his life.

What, she wondered, was so wonderful about having a river named for him?

31

Once more the peace of Sagamore Hill healed and restored Theodore, but before long, Edith was saying good-by again. He was rushing off to Washington to lecture on the South American expedition before the National Geographic Society. Mid-term elections were coming up. When he returned home, Progressive Party leaders began coming for conferences just as they had done in the old days. They wanted his advice and urged him to run for governor of New York. He made a speech or two, but he was ordered by his doctor to rest. That had never been easy for him to do; it was more difficult now that a great war threatened to engulf Europe. He warned that Germany was about to invade Belgium. If that happened, the United States would not be safe any longer. She must be ready to defend herself, because the Kaiser would not be content to limit his game of war to his own borders.

No one in the government seemed to be listening to Roosevelt's warning, but by the summer of 1914 his foreboding was justified. Belgium's neutrality was violated by the German army, the Kaiser was on the way to Paris, devastating every village and farm that lay between.

President Wilson declared the neutrality of America. At first, T.R. backed him, but the horror of the invasion of Belgium disturbed his sleep, and he began writing articles about it. Gradually, he came out against Wilson's neutrality as it dawned upon him that Germany would not stop short of total European conquest. This brought down upon his head the fury of the American

German-language newspapers that had formerly supported him. The pacifists added their scorn. His was a lone voice demanding that America's defenses be strengthened, but his country was in no mood to see things the way they really were.

Two and a half years after the outbreak of the Great War, the views of the ex-President were still ignored. For him, it was a period of loneliness and anguish. Anguish, because a country as great as the United States was helpless and unprepared. The nation was content to grow prosperous and fat from the war, but the war would not come closer than that, would it? When Roosevelt cried, "Be prepared!" critics screamed "Militarism!" Patiently, he continued to go before the people, explaining that it was not militarism to build up the nation's defenses.

In May, 1915, the *Lusitania* was sunk by a German submarine. 1,000 Americans aboard the liner lost their lives. Roosevelt had been closer to the facts than President Wilson. With fresh conviction, the Colonel indicted the "professional pacifists, the flubdubs and the mollycoddles." He wrote the Secretary of War, Newton D. Baker, that he was prepared to lead a division of men who were volunteering for service under his command. The astounding thing was that over *two hundred thousand* Americans wanted to follow T.R. into the front lines. A new rallying cry arose when his plan was described in the papers: "Send Roosevelt to France!"

Even Clemenceau, the great French statesman, begged Wilson to send the Colonel. "No other American has such a hold on the French imagination," he wrote. One American editor, a Democrat, said, "The appearance of an ex-President of the United States leading American soldiers to the battlefront would electrify the world."

Roosevelt himself told his sister that he realized he was too old to go, that he wouldn't last. But that did not matter. He could arouse the belief that America was going to help.

Finally, Wilson gave his reply. The Colonel had gone to him in person as a last resort, and the country had been waiting for the decision. He refused T.R.'s offer. His curt words to the press indicated that he did not trust the motives of America's most illustrious volunteer, nor his military experience. War had changed since the charge up the San Juan Hills. The romance of it, the gallantry, was gone. This war was not for aging ex-Presidents.

There was some consolation, however. On the same day Wilson turned Roosevelt down, he announced that General Pershing would take an expeditionary force of regulars to France. At last, President Wilson had admitted the necessity to act.

Remaining at home, far away from the action, must have been the most difficult thing yet required of Theodore. But his sons were in training, which gave him some sense of participation. Ted, a major, was in command of the first battalion of the 26th Infantry of Regulars in the First Division. Archie was a lieutenant in the same outfit. Kermit, a captain, was in the battalion of Sappers, and Quentin was flying with a French squadron. Their father must live out his dreams in them; against everything in his nature, he must stay safely at home while they fought in his place.

His sons were constantly in his thoughts. At least once a week he wrote to each one. When word came back of their bravery and leadership, he beamed with pride. The old vitality, the boyishness were gone but not his sincere sentiment. He advised Quentin to correspond more regularly with his girl friend if he expected her to wait for him. "This is the thirty-second anniversary of Mother's and my engagement," he wrote. "And I really think I am just as much in love with her as I was then — she is so wise and good and pretty and charming."

In 1918, the Republicans began courting Theodore as in days gone by. Wilson's popularity was waning. By election time in 1920, the Colonel would probably be the choice of the G.O.P. once more, to carry it to victory.

Roosevelt was not interested. Fever was his enemy now. The abscess from his leg injury in Brazil had never healed, and required an operation. He came through it all right, and the fever subsided but, back at Sagamore, the only thing he or Edith could think about was the war. The boys were all near the firing line. If one was killed, the parents wondered what they could say to each other, what they would do. "I feel as though I were a hundred years old," Theodore said to Edith one day.

The nights of sleeplessness and the days of suspense dragged by. There was no way to anticipate the news. Some of it was good: "Kermit has been decorated for gallantry in action." Some of it was bad: "Archie has been wounded; one arm paralyzed." Pershing wrote in person of Ted's outstanding abilities and his promotion to lieutenant-colonel.

On July fourth, the papers headlined a story about American pilots bringing down seven enemy planes. Quentin was in the thick of that combat. Ten days later he was shot down.

Was Quentin dead, or had he landed behind the lines and been taken prisoner? They would not know for at least three days.

On the afternoon of July 20th, Theodore Roosevelt received a delegation from the Japanese Red Cross. He welcomed them to Sagamore and, after a little speech, served tea. As the guests were leaving, a reporter asked in a voice the others could not hear, if any word had come of Quentin.

"Yes," Theodore answered, reaching into his coat pocket for a crumpled telegram. "I received this twenty minutes before you arrived." The reporter read a message of sympathy from President Wilson. Quentin was dead.

The life that was dearer to Roosevelt than his own was gone.

32

In 1918 the Great War ended, and Ted, Archie and Kermit returned home.

On November 11, the day the Armistice was signed, their father had gone back to the hospital, this time with inflammatory rheumatism. The pain kept him in bed, but he did not allow it to keep him from caring for his correspondence and other interests. His wish to be home for Christmas came true. The family gathered at Sagamore Hill for the traditional celebration, which for the first time was subdued by sadness. Even though there were grandchildren and pets to brighten the scene, it would never be the same without Quentin.

The days that followed were contented ones for Theodore, but most of them were spent in bed. The light was restful in the northwest bedroom. Edith read to him, or he read to her. He was with the one he loved best, in the place dearest to them both.

On the evening of January 5, 1919, he went to sleep rather early. Since Quentin's death, there had been a pensive tone in his voice, but on this day, Ethel's little girl had entertained him. He had teased and laughed with her.

During the night, he died, peacefully.

From all over the world, tributes came to Edith and the family — from kings and rulers, from President Wilson and the entire Congress of the United States, from the people great and humble. But none was more appropriate than the green and living tribute expressed by the American Boy Scouts. Each troop planted one or more trees in his memory.

Theodore Roosevelt would have liked that.